To Pen...

Happy ...

Days

101 Naked Confessions

of a Gay Hairdresser

Terry Wilson

Terry Wilson

101 Naked Confessions of a Gay Hairdresser

ISBN 978-1-907308-09-3

A catalogue copy is available at the British Library

www.hairorganics.com

Published by Compass Publishing
www.compass-publishing.com

Printed in Great Britian

The Gossip About 101 Naked Confessions...

"On a bad day or just an ordinary day, Terry's book sends a beam of light to hearten the soul and make you smile. His observations on life are amusing, quirky and endearing, always affectionate and informative. The same warmth and ability to make one feel part of the family is one of the reasons I come to his salon. I am made to feel welcome and safe in professional hands, in a laid back way."
Louisa Miles ~ Theatrical Agent

"Terry's wit, wisdom and willingness to share both his highs and his lows through his stories bring a smile to my face - and sometimes a tear to my eye - every time. The only thing better than reading his words is hearing Terry's stories in person at his amazing Hair Organics salon in Notting Hill. Although you can't carry Terry around with you in person for inspiration so maybe this book wins out after all!"
Jo Kearins ~ Proud Kiwi, Hair Organics Fan and Associate Director at Luther Pendragon

"You can't imagine how snowed under my days are with words sometimes. But I always make time to read what Terry writes because he has the power to make me smile and laugh out loud. He makes me feel part of a community of dedicated people who celebrate life's shallows, depths, shipwrecks, cakes and wasn't there something about a camel once?"
Mary Fenwick ~ Writer, coach, fundraiser

"I so enjoyed this book. I have known Terry for a long time and I can just hear him telling these stories. It is funny, easy to read and thought provoking. I live by his tips for looking after hair. It really is a MUST read."
Victoria Whittaker

"The daily snippets of fun keep me sane and are a joyous distraction from my normal work routine. I look forward to tales of Notting Hill, Ibiza, camel rides across the desert and the latest salon offers.

For me, the salon is a home from home and the team is like family. You have been through all my boyfriend sagas and family health challenges over the years - we cry and we laugh, but most of all we have fun and I come out looking and feeling good."
Ros Rayman ~ Lawyer and stalker of Terrence for the last 15 plus years

"I love Terry and Kat's book. It's funny, clever, informative and full of personality. The book gives a big, smiling, accountable face to the salon, which shows they care. Yes, I get they're selling without 'selling', they're marketing to me to attract business - hell yeah! Make no apologies for wanting to make a buck! Yet they do it in such a way that everyone wins. They teach me something and make me smile, not least for the spelling mistakes or typos, but because of the very real, genuine people behind it. I love coming to Hair Organics because their skill, processes and products ensure I have great hair but I'm not poisoned by dangerous hair dyes and nasty chemicals, which is extremely important to me."
Simone Lanham-Sewell ~ Director, Incognito Artists
www.incognitoartists.com

"I'm so excited at the prospect of a book! Gosh, I never thought I'd know an author let alone that he would be one of my best friends.

And that's the point - I get to chat to Terry as a friend when I wish. The information in the book is for all your lovely clients, but also feels like it's just for me! Does that make sense?!? How clever you are in enveloping us all in your wisdom and passing on funny stories and anecdotes. It's just as if we are sitting in my kitchen in Liverpool, over a bottle of red and some lovely food! Well done and long may it all continue."
Lou Cross

"I met the team a year ago following a Google search for hairdressers in Notting Hill. I had moved to the area to save a few quid and during my time there had a few new experiences, from understanding first hand the term 'no room to swing a cat' to having an amazing hairdressing time at Hair Organics.

I had my first consultation with Nathan, which went on for over ten minutes. I arranged to return the following day feeling comfortable about the prospect of starting a new relationship.

And a relationship it is, even though I now live in Australia. The salon I go to now uses the same products but the atmosphere is just not the same. However, I know I can recreate the atmosphere by reading this book. And I close my eyes and take myself back to Notting Hill. Thank you for everything. I am being good and have stopped using products that damage my hair."
Yvette Lewington

"It's no mean feat to send out this sort of email three or four times a week and to keep it fresh, funny and something that I want to read instead of putting straight in the bin. I think the reason they're so readable is that they are all Terry-tastic; by this I mean I feel like I'm reading something from Terry personally (whom I adore obvs) and not some forced made up marketing shit. I like the way you also sometimes include comments from customers in the next email.

And why do I come to the salon? I've known Terry for a few years, from right back when he used to venture down to south London on his trusty bicycle to do haircuts for my friend and me after we'd had our babies and didn't have the time or energy to go anywhere else. Ah, those happy days of washing my own hair in the bath then sitting in the kitchen chatting with Terry in between bursts of tending to screaming newborns. And then what do you know, he goes off and sets up his own salon. But it didn't change him; the only thing that was different was that someone else washed our hair and the beautiful Gillian looked after us. On top of that, Terry is the only person who can cut/colour my hair in such a way that I feel amazing when I walk out. It's a true gift. Long live Hair Organics and all who sail in her."
Rachel Husband

"Terry is a master storyteller. He's witty and thoughtful, with a sharp eye for the hilarious. His stories are my coffee break - far better than a custard cream."
Florence Miller, Environmentalist

"Having had to colour my hair from an early age, I've become very aware of the dangers of chemical dyes. In fact, my pursuit of chemical-free products was something that led me into working in the world of beauty. After much research, I found Hair Organics in 2009. Since then, I have not only been a loyal client but also represented them as a PR. Why? Because I believe in what they do and how they do it! Co-Founder Terry Wilson truly is a diamond in the rough and a trailblazer in the world of organic hairdressing. Not only is he warm, charismatic and extremely charming, but he's also a hugely knowledgeable and talented hairdresser."

Edwina Wynyard, MD of Amazing PR

Acknowledgements

Terry would like to thank: My two wives, Kay my ex-wife and mother of my two lovely non-hairdressey-at-all daughters, and Jon my now-partner for putting up with me after the show is over each day.

Kat would like to thank: My handbrake and long-time husband, Kelvin, for being proud of me. And my daughter Heléna who makes me proud.

We would both like to thank the following individuals for their support and wisdom: Gavin and Su Robins, Beata Jostmeier, Jon McCulloch aka the EBG, Den Lennie, and Daniel Field.

We would also like to thank our fabulous collection of Hair Organics Notting Hill Staff for their passion, creativity and show-stopping performances.

And the **biggest thanks is reserved for our wonderful Hair Organics Notting Hill clients.** Without whom the gossip could not be shared.

Contents

Contents

Foreword

by Daniel Field

I have known Terry for many years. He has worked as a freelance hairdresser at my salon in London's West End twice. In the beginning he was very part time as he also worked as a session stylist, providing the makeup and hair styling on glamorous photoshoots across London.

Terry's true passion is transformation, and he uses a combination of excellent vision and his mature personality to coax the flower from everyone he works with, whether this is a top model or one of his many clients.

When Terry returned to my salon after a few years, he worked more days and I got to know him far better, recognising both the breadth of expertise and the uniqueness that he has to offer. Terry is gay, but he is also a father so he is able to temper his flamboyancy, creativity and his willingness and guts to push the boundaries image wise with his fatherly practicality and common sense. The result is a slow, sensitive confidence that emerges from each client as she quite literally blossoms in time and in every way, both inside and out. His skill, integrity, good taste and common sense all come together.

He called me some years back to tell me that he and Kat were opening the first of hopefully many organic salons. And when he asked me if I would like to provide my natural hair products, which I first started developing back in 1981, and my experience to help with this new project called Hair Organics, I immediately said YES!

Over these years, I have gotten to know Kat, too. She is indeed *'The Queen of Everything'*, but I think I should explain more about what this means to me. First and foremost, Kat is a discerning client. She literally loves perfection and does nothing half-heartedly. She ensures that her fellow clients get what she wants from the Hair Organics experience herself, and that is perfection. I often help with specialist training at the salon and Kat is there at every session I provide. She is an excellent businesswoman, but she wants to learn as if she was a hairdresser, too. There is a clear, calm focus in her that is clearly *'project led'*. Everyone who fits into the life and development of Hair Organics fits into each project so it's quickly clear who is coming on the journey and who will drop off.

I believe in Hair Organics. It is already far more than a *'gay hairdresser'* and *'The Queen of Everything'*, getting together and starting a hair salon. The partners have a sophisticated philosophy where their total respect for each individual client is clearly expressed in their hair and health. They also show respect to animals, using products that haven't been tested on them, and the environment. These all sit very comfortably together as a lifestyle experience, which is reflected both in the elegant and classy salon and the education each client is provided with. They get the choice to continuously develop their personal image, which gives them confidence to enjoy throughout their everyday life.

Daniel Field

Daniel Field

www.danielfield.net

Introduction

Hey!

I know you.

You are probably a woman over the age of 35, quite possibly with a partner and children.

You are good at your job and have had a varied and fulfilling career. You are busy with your work, kids, parents, partner and friends and have little time to indulge yourself. When you do find that time, you are not always comfortable taking it just for yourself. You feel guilty and think that you should be doing something for someone else. It can take you a while to relax when you are being pampered, but afterwards you feel great and refreshed and vow to do it more often.

You like to dine out, explore new places, experience new things and delight in showing your children how the world works.

You care about your health and the health of your family. You exercise regularly as your body is changing. You are beginning to get to grips with the deeper issues of life, such as your own mortality and how many people depend on you.

You have some great friends, and many of them have been by your side for years. They are very similar to you and you call on them for favours, which you return without hesitation. But mostly you are very independent and like to handle everything yourself.

You like to look good. It makes you feel confident. You dress well in quality pieces mixed with high-street brands. But you do have a favourite pair of jeans that get a regular workout.

You hair is also important to you and you know that when it's not right it prevents you from being the confident person you want to be.

You like to have fun and be amused. You do not suffer fools or constant negativity. You like to build relationships over time. These are based on trust, and once you have this you are extremely loyal.

I'm Terry Wilson and welcome to my world. A world where your needs are met when it comes to establishing a trusting relationship with your hairdresser, a relationship where your hair in particular can achieve its optimal health.

I wrote '*101 Naked Confessions of a Gay Hairdresser*' along with my business partner, Kat Smith. It's actually a collection of daily emails that I send out to my clients at my salon in London's Notting Hill - people just like you. Yes, it is marketing, and yes, we do use them to sell our products and services (horror!), but, as you will see, it is done in such a way that you will actually enjoy being sold to. That being said, the main point of these emails or confessions is to entertain, amuse and inform. Oh, and to build a relationship with my readers so that

I am not just another hairdresser that you might see once every two months.

In the following pages you will learn more about me than my mother knows. You may also learn something about yourself and your own opinions and beliefs. You will certainly learn something about your hair.

How to use this book

I've designed this book for you to keep in your handbag and dip in and out of. It's to entertain and amuse you on the tube, on your lunchbreak, or even on the loo if that's your thing. The confessions are short and sweet and they are all my own opinion. Throughout the book there are tips about how to get your hair into optimal condition, and I've also added some resources for you at the back. Yes, I am selling hair care and hair care products - that's my business. One thing to note is that although I enjoy hearing from my customers, feedback regarding how I run my business is irrelevant to me. I do what I do because it works. To coin a much-used phrase *'the results speak for themselves'*.

Just saying.

Speak soon.
Terry xxx

How It All Began...

In 2007, I was invited to take part in a charity fundraising day at a friend's salon in Notting Hill. For one Sunday every year, she gave all the money she raised to charity for orphaned children, which she had helped to set up. She needed volunteers to cut hair and I was happy to help out.

The salon was situated just off Notting Hill Gate, was fabulously quirky and I had a great day there. As we were sitting having a beer after closing time, I said to my friend in passing, *"If you ever want to sell this place, let me know."*

Eighteen months later - after another charity day had been and gone - my friend did phone to ask if I would be interested in buying her business. I had been freelancing for a few years and felt ready to put my own stamp on a salon again. My friend Kat had just had a baby and didn't want to go back to her corporate job. So I called her with an offer that I hoped she wouldn't be able to refuse.

"Do you want to buy a salon with me?" I asked. *"I'll be the brawn, and you can be the brains."*

And this is his how *Hair Organics Notting Hill* was born.

A Funky David Bowie Mullet

The thought of becoming a hairdresser didn't strike me until late into my college years. I studied arty subjects throughout high school, but I was so into sport, swimming and surf lifesaving, that the possibility of cutting hair for a living had simply never occurred to me.

Then, in the mid 70s, a hairdresser called Ron Potter turned up in my sleepy hometown of Blenheim, on New Zealand's South Island, to work in one of our biggest salons. (The population of Blenheim was only about 20,000 back then, but the town is now on the map for producing Marlborough wines.) Ron was from London and cut a rather exotic figure in small town New Zealand. He quickly became popular and opened his own salon. Anyone who was anyone flocked there, even me! The salon always had a real buzz about it, and I think that's why I liked it so much.

As I got to know Ron better, he asked what I wanted to do with my life, and he even offered to train me. He had it all: the beautiful wife (who was also the receptionist, very Beverly Sassoon, darling!), the salon, a fleet of staff and a sports car. He walked the walk and talked the talk.

Around the same time, I took a trip to Auckland to see my grandmother and brother, who was in the army and stationed there. We went to a shopping centre, and I decided to get a haircut in an open-plan salon. The glamorous stylist whipped my head back in the basin before shampooing and blow drying my hair into a funky David Bowie style mullet. I loved it!

I remember that it cost $12. I had to go and find my brother outside to get an extra $2 as I only had $10. My brother didn't recognise me with my new *'do'* and walked straight past me. Oh, the power of a new haircut!

Back at college, I had to do the usual interview with the careers officer. When I mentioned that I was interested in hairdressing, he immediately picked up the phone and rang a barbershop only a five-minute walk away from my home. What a result, I started the next week! So, while my head was still spinning and I was trying to collect my thoughts, I already had my career mapped out for me.

Speak soon,
Terry xxx

P.S. Not long into that job I quickly realised that doing pensioner trims and selling tobacco wasn't what I wanted to do for the rest of my life. I started to look around for other options.

Sets, Perms & Farah Fawcett

After six weeks of working in the barbershop, a job vacancy came up at Blenheim's leading hairdressers, Vogue Salon.

Despite its status in the town, I didn't even know where it was. That's how wet behind the ears I was back then.

After a bit of a search, I went there after work one Monday. The boss, Judith Bythell, wasn't there and four of the salon girls were laughing hysterically at the front of shop as they made prank calls to their boyfriends. I told them that I would like to see Judith about the apprenticeship and one of them (whom I later nicknamed *'Bossy Roseanne')* said, *"But she doesn't want a BOY!"*

I left with my tail between my legs and thought no more of it. I could always go to see Ron Potter, I thought, but then there *was* something a little strange about him.

More on that later…

Three days later, I received a call at the barbershop from Judith at Vogue. She asked me if I was going to come back. I told her what had happened and she said to come and see her regardless of what Roseanne said.

I started as the 'boy' apprentice the following week. My five years at Vogue doing shampoos and sets, perms, hair-ups, and Farah Fawcett style blow-waves were the most fantastic years I could ever have spent as an apprentice.

Many mad years later, here I am here with my own salon in Notting Hill, London. Who would have thought it?!

So what happened to Ron Potter? He went mad and preached religion to all his clients. His wife left him, he lost the salon and became a gardener.

My instincts were right. Turned out he wasn't even from London...

Probably Bognor Regis!

Speak soon,
Terry xxx

How Kat And I Met

Speed dating.

Have you ever tried it?

I haven't.

Although I did go to an event with Kat once where there were about 150 businesswomen in a room, and I was the only male. We had to do this 'speed networking' type of thing, but that's a different story.

I was chatting to a good friend about his experiences of speed dating. And I am guessing it is different for a guy than a girl, but his observations about it could pretty much sum up everything in life. What I mean is, there are some things you need to do to be successful at speed dating which you can pretty much carry over to be successful in the rest of your life:

1. Don't be desperate – this gives off the wrong vibes; it scares people and pushes them away.

2. Prepare to laugh at yourself – if you can do this, people will be more relaxed around you. You will also be more prepared to take risks as you 'laugh in the face of failure'.

3. Smile and look people in the eye – you *are* interesting, you will find something to say. 4. Get a good haircut – hahahaha made that one up! But still…

Actually, dating and finding a good hairdresser are very similar processes. It takes quite a bit of work on both sides to build a relationship and establish trust, and believe me, a good hairdresser will understand this implicitly and not rush into anything. We're just not that type of boy!

It reminds me of how Kat and I met. She had just moved to my town for a job and was on the lookout for a new hairdresser, just one of a long list of stressful things you have to do when you move. Her husband, Kelvin, came to me first. Good trick that, get a guy to come in first and see how his haircut and experience goes. Kelvin went home and raved about me (of course) and so Kat made the leap and came to me, too. We got on really well and I was her hairdresser for four years before I decided to head off to the UK to get some experience. I initially told everyone that I was going for six weeks to see some of the world, experience life in another country and get ideas on fashion and hair for my salon in New Zealand. Oh boy, did I have some fun.

When I got back to New Zealand, I told Kat: *"I had such a great time in London and loved it so much that I am selling the salon here and moving there for good. And, by the way, I'm gay"*. She replied: *"Tell me something I didn't know."*

So I sold the salon, 'divorced' over 300 loyal customers and headed over to London town. I lost touch with Kat then and a lot of my other friends in New Zealand; London just consumed me. Fast forward to a year later and I am working in a salon in Soho. One of Daniel Field's salons actually. And as I glance out the window, there they are on the footpath, Kat and Kelvin, waving maniacally at me. They had just been exploring the area and happened to be walking down that street by chance.

It's so good to catch up with people you know after a long absence. Kat became my client again – I always knew she was a stalker – and the rest is history. And it's also the present and future.

Speak soon,

Terry xxx

We Are Royals

I took my business partner Kat and Gill (my mad Canadian receptionist) to see a play called *The Audience* the other night. It was being screened live at The Gate Cinema in Notting Hill.

Helen Mirren played Queen Elizabeth II, as she does so well, and the story was about the weekly audiences that she has given to prime ministers since she was crowned in 1952. She has seen 12 different heads of government come and go during her reign, which adds up to a lot of meetings!

It was a fabulous production so do go and see it if you get the chance. For me, the *'Wow'* moments came while witnessing Ms. Mirren conducting super-quick costume changes on stage. We saw her transform from the Queen in her 60s, to how she looked in her 20s, 50s, 30s and back to her 60s again. She had six different wigs, which, along with her clothes, transformed her look in seconds.

It was *magic*.

This got me to thinking about how easy it is to completely alter your look by changing your hair colour or style. You can become someone *completely different* in a matter of minutes. And even though you are fundamentally the same person inside, the way you look can change the way you act.

This is why actors use hairstyles and costumes in their craft.

Clever.

This is also why I love my job so much. I revel in watching a transformation take place.

So, dare you brave a new look today?

Speak soon,
Terry xxx

P.S. Oh, and I didn't hesitate to remind Kat and Gill that I had met the Queen and tried out to be her hairdresser. Read on for this particular royal story…

She Keeps Her Rollers In A Shoebox!

Let me spill the beans about the day I met the Queen.

It was a decade ago now, but what a memorable day.

The powers that be at Buckingham Palace were looking into recruiting a new hairdresser in case the current one decided to retire, and they asked me to go along for a trial.

On the day of the annual Garter Day parade, which takes place in June, I was invited to Windsor Castle to shadow the current hairdresser, Sharon.

"Welcome to the madhouse," said one of the butlers by way of a greeting. When I finally got to the Queen's dressing room, she met me wearing a red polka dot dress and slippers!

She was delightful and there was a lot of joking and laughter. Prince Charles walked in at one point, which was all a bit surreal for someone from small town New Zealand. At the same time, it felt very normal, too.

I was given the *'Royal Rollers'* to hold as I assisted Sharon while she set the Queen's hair. The rollers were kept in an old shoebox along with a comb, a brush, some hairpins, a hairnet and some hairspray.

And there was no fancy massage chair for the Queen to

relax in while she had her head back in the basin, either. Her Majesty bent over a sink and held a towel to her face while she had her hair washed. Although she did sit under a 1960s style hood dryer once the rollers were in, one thing is the same the world over when it comes to having your hair done, and that's the flicking through of a magazine. The Queen's was *Horse & Hound*, of course!

It was a great day and The Queen even acknowledged me when she passed in the parade.

Sharon decided not to leave in the end, so I didn't get the job. But I think that that was probably for the best, otherwise Hair Organics Notting Hill would never have come to life…

That shoebox really bugged me though. Even when economising, there is no excuse not to have the right tools for the job.

So what are the best tools?

Keep reading and I will give you the royal answer!

Speak soon,
Terry xxx

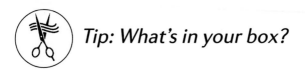 *Tip: What's in your box?*

Ooh er missus.

Not like that!

Here's what I suggest:

A wide-toothed comb or a brush with plastic bristles (like a Tangle Teezer) to comb out wet hair and distribute product through it evenly.

Sectioning clips. When blow-drying your hair, it is best to do it in sections. These clips (also known as alligator clips) hold the hair out of the way while you work. This will give you a more polished finish than if you just run your brush through large chunks of hair willy-nilly.

Brush. There are many types of brushes for many types of hair - too many to go into here - but as a guide, synthetic bristles are easier to get through the hair than natural ones are (although natural bristles will give a better shine). Always keep your brush clean and free from hair.

Hair dryer. Terms such as Nano or Ionic sound fancy, but - in my opinion - buying a hair dryer with these words in the title won't change your end result. It's more important to use your hair dryer correctly, along with the right products. This way you will avoid damaging your hair. Choose a hair dryer that is light and has a variable speed of airflow. If you have curly hair, make sure that it has diffuser nozzle. If your hair is straight, choose one with a concentrator nozzle.

Absorbent hair towel. Squeeze excess moisture out of your hair – never rub!

Hairbands. Please use plastic covered bands with no metal joiners. Match the colour of your bands to your hair; there is no excuse for wearing your four-year-old daughter's pink 'scrunchie'!

Grips. Pick kirby grips and match them to your hair colour for hiding in your hair up hairstyles.

And that's the basics.

Add to the list if you are looking to regularly change your style. By all means use *hot air stylers*, *curling wands* and *straighteners*, but remember that the formula for healthy hair is to use these *sparingly*.

Drag (Swimming) Queen

It's been a bit quiet of late. Unfortunately, I have been out of action with a bad case of sciatica; a pinched nerve in my lower back that causes pain all the way down my leg.

Have you ever experienced the type of pain that feels like a sledgehammer pounding your leg repeatedly?

No?

Well, let me just say that 2am at my house hasn't been a barrel of laughs lately.

The doctors (and I've been to a few recently) have said that it's not the worst case they've ever seen. Don't you find that annoying when all you care about is your own problem and not someone else's?! But rest and regular light exercise will help it to heal and get the muscles loose, which will relieve the pain.

I'm a keen swimmer, so I have been down to the pool putting in some laps. I swim with a float, called a pull buoy or drag float, between my legs to keep my back steady. This image tickled Kat, and she has been giggling about the *'Drag (Queen) Swimmer'* ever since.

Just as well she doesn't know that we call her *'The Queen of Everything'* in the salon.

Anyway, as I have been out of action, my time in the salon has been limited. The rest of the team is busier and appointments are becoming harder to come by. Lucky for you that we have an online booking system, so when you are awake at 2am and feeling sorry for me and my leg, you can still arrange to get beautiful hair.

Speak soon,
Terry xxx

Here's One I Made Earlier

Last Friday, I received an email asking me if I wanted to present a hair care product on a TV shopping channel called *Ideal World*.

I've been on TV before, so it's no surprise that people think I am made for it…obviously, with my personality and great looks, I am destined to be famous!

My first time on *'the box'* took place about a decade ago. I was doing the hair of Jeni Barnett, the host of the erstwhile TV programme, *Good Food Live.*

Because of the timing of the recordings, the studio would send a cab for me early in the morning. Well, on this particular early start, the cabbie turned to me and asked if I was famous.

"Not yet," I replied.

"Well, you're a lot nicer that the famous girl I went to pick up at 1am," the cabbie continued.

"She didn't answer my call when I got to her house, so I had to knock on the door. When she opened it she was stark naked…it was only that weird Bjork bird."

I killed myself laughing.

"I'm glad it wasn't me who knocked," I remarked.

"I've seen Bjork in the buff, but you're much better looking," the cabbie replied.

Thanks...I think.

I bet London cabbies get to see some sights that they would rather forget. I wonder if any of them have written a book. It would certainly be a bestseller.

I don't know if you ever saw *Good Food Live*, but the format was similar to many of the food shows that are now on every channel. Guest *'sleb'* chefs were invited on to share one of their favourite recipes and chat about themselves.

The show also had a segment on baking at home. Three members of the public (one of them me in this instance) were selected to make a similar dish, albeit from three different recipe books.

In our case, it was a cheesecake.

Mine turned out to be a chocolate one.

We had to buy our own ingredients and mine cost me exactly £11. Some other poor woman got a pumpkin cheesecake recipe that cost £33!

I duly baked the cheesecake, delivered it to the security guard at the studios and waited for my moment of fame. When it arrived, the three of us trooped in and sat on the sofa in the studio, explaining what our recipe was, how much it cost and how easy it was to make, etc. Then Jeni and whatever *'sleb'* was on that day (it was a camp air steward from a reality show about the Russian

Airline, *Aeroflot* - completely unmemorable) got to have a taste test.

They rated mine quite highly, so I was pleased with myself.

Straight after the tasting the cameras went off and the crew descended like gannets.

'Poof', my cheesecake was gone!

I didn't get so much as a sniff of it.

So much for my 10-seconds of fame.

The show's producers didn't ask me back to do any more baking, and the show closed down not long after that.

Their loss!

But I do love cooking and baking, and I still have the recipe book they gave me.

It's very simple. I'm a simple, made-for-TV kind of guy.

Speak soon,
Terry xxx

P.S. I moved on to more interesting TV roles after *Good Food Live.* Oh, the glamour!

The Joy Of The Burger

A couple of people have asked me to explain to them what is so great about a *Kiwiburger*. Well, back in the 1970s (if you remember them), a new burger was born in New Zealand. A traditional meat patty burger was enhanced by the addition of cheese, lettuce, onion, pickled beetroot, tomato, a pineapple ring *and* a fried egg.

Now, there is a lot of debate between connoisseurs of this delicacy about whether you should include the pineapple ring or the egg. Some like it with both, others with one or the other. However, in all cases, the beetroot remains a constant. I remember that the juice used to soak into the paper bag (no fancy burger boxes then), staining everything pink.

It's quite an art to eat one of these bad boys without it disintegrating in your hand, or finishing up with half the ingredients down your front.

While in New York, I have visited a burger bar called *Joy Burger*, which is owned my friend and client, Elizabeth.

Elizabeth is an amazing woman. She is related to a very well-known British retail tycoon, which means that her own accomplishments are often over looked. But she recently decided that she was going to buy a business in the States and become a businesswoman. After raising a family and doing a little bit of journalism, she wanted to make a change and do something for herself. As a woman in her 60s (ssshhh, a women never reveals her age), she raised the capital required and just went off and did it.

I am very proud of her considering that she had never bought a business before, didn't know what a profit and loss sheet was, and had no idea how to recruit or keep staff. If you are in New York, then definitely head to *Joy Burger* on 361 6th Avenue. They serve nice burgers, which are not too big as is the usual American way, and delicious handmade fries.

I am going to try and convince her to add the Kiwiburger to the menu!

Speak soon,
Terry xxx

Like Having Red-Hot Pokers Prodded Into Your Scalp

I love sharing my experience with younger generations who are keen to learn the craft of hairdressing.

For the last six weeks, I have been training six young women how to do a proper *Indian Head Massage*, which despite its name incorporates massage of the shoulders, upper arms, neck, scalp and face. It's a therapeutic massage and we can incorporate some of the techniques, especially on the scalp, at the basin when you are having your hair conditioned or treated.

The six students had so much fun and were grateful to learn some new techniques, which I found very rewarding. It means that they will give their clients added value at the salon. It was also gratifying to be surrounded by youth and beauty!

The last night of the training was on a Monday, so my partner Jon, Kat *'The Queen of Everything'* and I posed as models for the trainees to do their final assessment on. Now Jon loves massage and I have even trained him how to do a great one for others. So he was really enjoying having massage after massage, as well as giving instructions on how to improve the pressure, etc.

But Kat, well, she's a different kettle of fish. She hates head massage and reckons it's like having red-hot pokers repeatedly prodded into her scalp.

So you can imagine how she felt when I told her that she had to be a model for three of the trainees!

Speak soon,
Terry xxx

P.S. Fair play to her, Kat tolerated it really well, and - secretly - I think she enjoyed it. But it reminded me that what is *enjoyable for one person may not be for the next*, so we need to tailor-make the salon experience to each individual.

Tip: Train your stylist early

So here's a tip, relating to the previous story – tell your stylist what you like. Tell them before they start, and tell them during the service. If massage is not your thing, that should be okay with them. If it is something you like, tell them also. A good stylist should listen to your wants and adapt to them. This may seem very obvious, but the number of clients I have had who have left their previous stylist because they didn't listen could fill up my big black book.

Blind, But Still Can See

Kat and I are at a two-day conference in London. We are learning some cool stuff about how to make our business better.

Yesterday our guest speaker was Liz Jackson, founder of a marketing company called *Great Guns*. Liz has appeared on the TV programme *The Secret Millionaire,* starring as the secret millionaire, of course.

She started her company when she was 25 and has turned it into a multi-award winning, multi-million pound business. She has been recognised by the Queen with an MBE, and is also raising two small children.

Liz is a fantastic speaker, very down-to-earth, funny and self-deprecating. If you get the chance to hear her speak, jump at it.

But the real inspiration in her story is that a few months after she launched her company, Liz went completely blind. Now most people would pack it all in and retreat in the face of that kind of adversity. Liz, on the other hand, decided that it would not change who she was, or her dream of having a successful business.

I can't imagine what it would be like not to have seen my children, not to know what my partner looks like (Liz's tells her he is the best-looking man in the world!), or be able see the faces of my employees when I am asking them to do something! It astounds me that she has been able to set up a business, get clients, wade through legislation and employ, train and motivate staff while dealing with a disability.

The biggest message I got from Liz though was that her coping mechanism is to be grateful for everything that she does have. She says thanks for it every morning.

That's pretty cool.

There are things out there that we have no control over, but Liz has found a way to be grateful for the things that she does have power over. And that motivates her to be a positive person every day.

So I am going to be grateful for everything that I have, including you.

Thank you for being a great client.

So, on the subject of things that *you have control over*, one of them is great hair condition.

My team and I are working towards getting your hair into its best ever condition. You can shorten the time to get to that point by indulging in a conditioning treatment, which is time never wasted on the path to glossy and easy to manage hair.

Speak soon,
Terry xxx

P.S. I was also impressed that Liz left school with no qualifications. She had no idea what she was going to do in life, but her first boss saw her strengths and allowed her to use them in his business, which helped it to grow. This just goes to show that good bosses are worth their weight in gold. Investment in people always pays off. Just like investment in your hair pays off, too!

When You Think You Know Someone

On the second day of our conference, I was really surprised and dead chuffed to see Kat being invited up on stage, in front of 200 people, to speak about her success in building the salon's marketing structure.

For five minutes and 13 seconds (I filmed it), she spoke of implementing what we had learnt from seminars over the last year to make our business better for you, our great clients, and for the staff.

Her speech brought tears to my eyes.

To cap it off, loads of people came up to me afterwards to comment on how well Kat had spoken.

That made me so proud.

I've known Kat for nearly 19 years now, and it's always cool when you learn something new about someone you thought you knew well.

I guess it is the same with knowing yourself. You surprise yourself sometimes by doing things you thought you couldn't.

That brings to mind a great quote I heard by Henry Ford, the founder of the *Ford Motor Company.*

He said: *"If you think you can, or if you think you can't, you are absolutely right."*

So the question is: *can you really get your hair into great condition?* The answer is that we can get it there for you, but you have to take the leap.

Speak soon,
Terry xxx

P.S. After Kat spoke people asked me what I actually did. I told them that *"I'm an expert"*. More on that to come...

Ask The Expert

After two days at the seminar, I was shattered and pleased to get back in the salon to do what I do best.

Don't get me wrong. I love getting out, learning new things, improving my knowledge and sharing inspiration with others. But coming back to the salon and doing things that I can do blindfolded is equivalent to having a rest.

I discovered a few things about myself at the seminar. One of them is that *I am an expert.*

One of the sessions was run by Dr. Adrian Atkinson, chairman of the business psychology consultancy, *Human Factors International.* He also wrote and starred in the BBC TV series *Mind of a Millionaire.* He asked us to fill in a very short survey designed to show us what type of business personality we have.

Well, mine came out as *Expert.* I am someone who recognises the value in getting processes right, and I focus on achieving high-quality work. That makes me similar to James Dyson, of vacuum cleaner fame.

So now I have to tell the team the bad news.

I am 'The Expert'.

So I am *never wrong.*

Can't wait to see their faces when I let them know that!

Actually, it kind of makes sense to me. I am constantly looking at the best ways of doing things. Some of the techniques that we use in the salon to highlight or colour hair are the result of me constantly working out the best and most effective ways to get fantastic results.

Speak soon,
Terry xxx

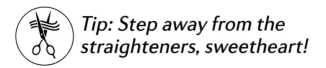 *Tip: Step away from the straighteners, sweetheart!*

There are only three ways that you can damage your hair, and once you know what they are you can prevent them from happening, find a repair or minimise the damage.

Chemical damage

You know that the packet of colour on the chemist shelf looks fab on that model, and your brain tells you that it will look just as good on you, and if you have hair like that your whole life will change and it will be just fantastic. The downside is that these colours still contain nasty chemicals that are not doing your hair any favours. The mere process of hair colouring, even the way we do it at the salon, creates some form of damage to your hair. The cuticle of the hair is forced open, the natural colour is stripped out and then new colour pigments are deposited. In the final stage, the cuticle is forced to close again. If your hair had nerves, you would have to have a general anaesthetic.

Environmental damage

The sun. That great big orb of life-force is great (when you see it), but over exposure to the sun strips moisture from the hair leaving it dry and brittle. Modern living in big cities plays havoc too, because pollution builds up on the hair and in the scalp. And don't get me started on hard water!

Heat and mechanical damage

Okay, Darling, step away from those straighteners! Constant use of high heat to achieve a style is just going to create issues. It's like over baking a cake – it's going to be dry and crumbly and not at all tasty. The same goes for roughing up your hair with a towel, or dragging a comb through tangles. And those little metal fasteners on hairbands should be banned!

Would You Ever Refuse Medical Treatment?

Last week, I was invited to a book launch.

I was honoured to attend as the book was written by one of our amazing clients, *Laura Bond.*

A while ago her mother was diagnosed with ovarian and uterine cancer and decided to refuse all medical intervention in favour of alternative, natural therapies. It sounds like a hard decision to make, but like everything, it is your decision how you treat your body, nobody else's. Laura started writing a blog about her mother's journey, their research and what they and others thought about what they were doing. This led to her book, *Mum's Not Having Chemo*, which is out now.

Along the way, Laura discovered us and interviewed me about our organic and mineral hair dye, and the impact that traditional hair dye has on people's long-term health.

You see, I don't just care about using products that will get your hair looking fantastic, I care about your health, and the health of my team, too. I am passionate about achieving great results without compromise. It means we have to work a bit differently from other salons, but it's worth it.

If you are interested in reading Laura's book (and my contribution in it), it's available to order on Amazon.

Also, if you know someone who is going through this illness and wants some advice about how to care for their hair, I would be happy to speak to them. Give the salon a call on 0207 229 6318. Sometimes it's the small things that can make a big difference.

Speak soon,
Terry xxx

P.S. One of our salon assistants, Beata, has just told us she is pregnant with her first child. Happy days! Now there is a whole new section of a department store that she can go shopping in. And she knows where she can get her hair dyed without harming her baby. *Hair Organics*, of course!

When 'Ask A Question' Means *Ask A Question*

Do you ever wonder why people don't follow instructions?

I find it so annoying.

I was at a seminar last week and there was an open floor Q & A session. This is where participants are invited up to the microphone to ask a question about anything from the seminar so far, to something that is troubling them in their business.

These sessions can be valuable if someone asks something that is relevant to what you are doing, and it gives you a chance to resolve any of your own burning issues.

The world would be perfect if that format was the case.

But in this instance, it wasn't.

Rather than ask a question, over half of the participants decided to launch into a full history of themselves and their business. The facilitator was very diplomatic, but if I had to hear, *"So what is your question?"* one more time…

Why do people do that?

In the end, the room was so warm (and we had just had lunch) that I dozed off.

Eventually Kat kicked me under the table.

She likes to keep me in my place.

So it's nice to come back from these seminars and receive emails from you which are *actually asking questions.*

Like this one, from our client, France:

First off, thank you guys for your regular emails. They always spread a smile on my face, even on Mondays! They also make me feel so special, like a preferred VIP!

I have to admit that last time I came over (yes, it was a while ago, I'll ask my boss for a raise) it was the ONLY hairdressing experience that I've actually genuinely enjoyed. It was also the ONLY time I've ever actually meant it when I said I liked my hair after the treatment.

So thank you for that, and for the coffee, biscuits, expert hands, loving care and listening ears.

Now is my time for a rewarding treat at your salon, and a chance to stand out in job interviews, and hopefully dates too!

To the point:

I'd like an appointment with a stylist for a semi-permanent, water-based colour, cut and finish, please. My preference is for Friday. (Friday night date in sight, you know…) Can you possibly squeeze me in?

Many thanks,

France

Now, apart from having a very cool name, France knows exactly what she wants. If you read the email carefully, you'll see that she understands that by getting her hair done by us, she is going to feel great on her date - and that's what counts. When your hair is right, you look and feel great, and great things happen.

Speak soon,
Terry xxx

Surely It's Not Time For A Divorce?

So I am up in Liverpool today. I took the slow train on Sunday, and I mean the slow train.

I could have walked it faster...even with my sciatica!

When I arrived at my friend, Lou's, she handed me a newspaper clipping that said the average woman will stay with a hairdresser longer than her husband. Typically, she will have a relationship with her hairdresser for 12.5 years, while the average marriage lasts only 11.5 years (*Source: Netvouchercodes.co.uk*).

We sat and had a giggle over this article, as it is exactly 12 and a half years since I started my first job in London working in Daniel Field's salon in Soho. From that day on, the journey I have been on in the hairdressing world has been crazy, mad, exciting, glamorous and hard work. I have taken clients along for the ride and most of the people from Daniel's salon have followed me all the way.

I am not saying it's time for a divorce.

It's a sad thing that marriages only last an average 11.5 years, but it's even sadder if you can't find a hairdresser for life!

When I sold my salon in New Zealand in 2000, it did feel as if I was divorcing 300 people (my clients). There was no easy way to say, *"I'm leaving you, now it's time for you to fend for yourselves in the big, scary, bad-hair-day world."*

A good hairdresser does more than produce great hair. They are your confidant, psychologist and travel advisor all rolled into one. So it figures that when you find a good one, you want to hang on to them. Kat, my business partner, did the extreme thing and followed me to London.

Stalker!

Relationships are built on trust, communication and respect. The same goes for the hairdresser/client relationship. You have to trust your stylist to do the right thing and not damage your hair or your look, which can ultimately harm your self-esteem. You have to be able to understand each other so that you can relay your needs and wants to your stylist knowing that they will be able to interpret them. There are not many professions where the touching of the head is required (in some cultures, the head is very sacred), so a great deal of respect is required.

Speak soon,
Terry xxx

Persistence Pays Off

I would like to introduce you to *Gleb*.

You might know Gleb already, but if you don't, he is our resident Estonian (and the only straight male on the team).

Gleb is a *great hairdresser.*

He is also very intense in his approach. He likes to research everything fully and when he gets an idea or an interest, he reads every article and buys every book there is that relates to it.

It can sometimes drive me nuts.

For example, he has just passed his driving test and is out on the roads. (If you see a blue-eyed Estonian coming at you, turn the corner quick!) But for the last year, during every spare moment he's had, Gleb has been learning the *Highway Code* in the back room of the salon. This book is now so dog-eared that it can't even be put on Amazon for 5p. If I have to see it again, I will cry!

When Gleb got his license he said: *"I was too confident for my first test. I thought I knew how to drive, but I failed. I was very nervous for my next test, so I was far more cautious. As a result, I passed."*

Fair play to Gleb. It's not easy learning something like the *Highway Code*, but it must be even harder when English isn't your first language.

I have driven on London roads and if I was Prime Minister for a day, my first thing would to ban the Hanger Lane gyratory and Hyde Park Corner. I would also put some ruddy signs up and more markings on the roads.

"Where is this going?" I hear you ask.

Well, I am proud of Gleb. His persistence pays off.

When he wants something, he goes out and gets it, no matter how long it takes. He's *very focused* and determined and he gets the job done.

This is a little bit like persisting with your hair when you know it's not right. It might be damaged, or the wrong colour, or the cut you like is growing out yet you want to keep growing it. There will always be a solution to the problem, you just need to do your research, focus, persist and put the time in.

I promise.

Speak soon,
Terry xxx

P.S. Gleb also said that as soon as he got his license, he found himself with a problem.

He was driving his wife Veera to Hastings when he realised that she has *'Back Seat Driver Syndrome'*. Veera is absolutely lovely, but it turns out that she knows how to drive better than Gleb.

"Terry, I have gained a license but lost a marriage," he told me.

Did I mention that Gleb has a unique sense of humour?

Being Blow-Dried By A 1000 Watt Hairdryer

Mr. Fix-It was in the salon this morning

One of our back-wash chairs was stuck in the up position and we couldn't get it down.

In life, there are only a few times that you want to be stuck in the up position - and this is not one of them!

When I bought the salon, nearly five years ago, I wanted to provide the best shampooing area possible. I imported these fancy Italian chairs that connected to our large basins and were built for comfort. The footrests come up and lift your legs until you are horizontal, which relieves pressure on your neck. The seat also pulses with air to give you a relaxing back massage - very decadent. When we opened we were the only salon in the UK to have these chairs.

At the time Mr. Fix-It arrived, I was talking to the team about Indian Head Massage. We massage your head when you are at the basin for two reasons. First, it helps you relax and contributes to your lovely experience in the salon. Second, it helps to massage the conditioner or treatment into your hair, helping it to penetrate the follicles and work better.

I love having my head massaged.

Some people don't.

As you know, Kat hates it.

As well as comparing it to being attacked by a red-hot poker, she says that it makes her want to crawl out of her skin. She claims that she would rather be blow-dried by a 1000 watt hairdryer than have any pressure on her head.

I think that she is being a bit over dramatic, but everyone's different.

Speak soon,
Terry xxx

P.S. In some cultures, like my native New Zealand Maori culture, the head is sacred. So we make sure that we treat your head with the greatest respect. And we want to know if massage is your thing, or if a comb-through and a rest in the chair is enough.

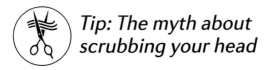 *Tip: The myth about scrubbing your head*

People have been trained to scrub their scalp to get it clean. It probably started as a young child, when they had an overzealous mum or grandma getting stuck in with some 'elbow grease' to give their hair a 'proper clean'. Well, hair does need to be cleaned, but the hard work should be done by the shampoo itself, not the 'elbow grease'. It should provide enough lather to gently cleanse the pollution, oil and product build-up (if you are using nasty ones) from each strand. Your scalp is a delicate area and the place where your hair grows from, so it needs to be maintained as an optimal environment. It needs to be moisturised, just like the rest of the skin on your body, not stripped completely bare of natural oil.

Does this sound familiar?

You jump in the shower and get your hair wet. Then you squeeze a liberal amount of shampoo on to your hand and start rubbing it on the top of your head. You give your head a really good scrub and get lots of lather going. You rinse and then repeat the process as per the instructions on the shampoo bottle, scrubbing away with the pads of your fingers. You rinse again and get that *'squeaky clean'* feeling, but by now your scalp feels a bit tight. So you grab the conditioner and squeeze another big dollop on to your hand and start rubbing it on the top of your head, relieving the tightness of the scalp but not really getting it to the ends. You pile your hair on top of your head while you exfoliate your face or shave your legs. Then you rinse.

While blow drying your hair, you find that the roots closest to the scalp are a bit flat and lifeless, and the ends of your hair are a bit dry, fuzzy or fly away.

What was wrong with that process?

Stay tuned.

3 Reasons Chefs Are Like Hairdressers

One of my favourite pastimes is to watch *Masterchef: The Professionals* on TV.

I love to cook and the standard of the food, the creativity and the competition on this show really inspires me.

It also makes me really hungry when I watch it, but that's another story.

As I was watching it last night, it struck me that there are a few parallels between being a chef and being a hairdresser.

Firstly, there is the creativity. Both jobs require the vision to create something different, beautiful and unique.

Then there is taking your vision and making sure that the end product is something that the customer will enjoy. A bad plateful of food is just as unpleasant as a bad head of hair.

And finally, there is the competition, whether that's being competitive with others or yourself.

And you thought that it was just a cooking show!

I love what I do, but if I had the chance to do it all again, I would open up a café and cook up a storm. Maybe that's what I will do when I retire. What would you do if you weren't doing what you do now?

Speak soon,
Terry xxx

P.S. Inspiration recently dragged me off the sofa and into the kitchen where I made two of my famous Christmas cakes. They are sitting at home and they get a drink of something from the top shelf every day, which will keep them moist and give them an edge. They will be ready to bring into the salon next week, where they will go very nicely with your cup of tea or coffee.

As Camp As Christmas

Yesterday, we put the Christmas decorations up in the salon.

I know, I know. You don't need reminding! It's only a month until Christmas!

Kat, Nathan and I did all the work. Or rather, Kat directed, Nathan fluffed up the greenery and I was sent out to buy some lights for the wreath in the window. I came back with the most colourful ones that I could find. I'm not sure they were quite what Kat had in mind for our classic, white-light theme, but hey, she could have gone out herself!

So the salon looks very festive and, as the big day approaches, I might just add some tinsel to the mirrors. Be warned, the closer it gets to Christmas, the camper it will get in the salon (and Kat won't be here to see it so we can get away with anything!).

Combined with my alcoholic Christmas cake and a few glasses of bubbly here and there, it is shaping up to be a bit of a naughty festive season.

Speak soon,
Terry xxx

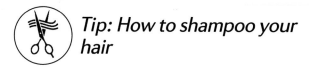 *Tip: How to shampoo your hair*

So, what is wrong with the shampoo-scrub-shampoo-scrub-condition process that I described in the last tip I gave you on page 68? You've been doing it for years, right?

The thing is, this cleaning process strips the scalp of all its natural oils. You have replaced the oils with the conditioner, but putting it on the roots is way too much for the scalp to handle. It is now weighing the hair down in the place you probably most want body, and the area you most want the conditioner to do its heavy duty work on - the dry ends - got missed out. If you have longer hair the natural oils often don't get a chance to travel down to the ends between shampoos, and this dries it out.

So how do you fix this?

It's very simple; you just need to reverse the process. Using a small amount of shampoo, gently cleanse the scalp but concentrate on making the shampoo work for your hair by getting it to lather on the strands. The first shampoo is really to break down any products, pollution and excess oils on the hair strands. You won't see a great amount of lather as this is the emulsifying stage. The next shampoo should produce a lather that gives the hair a deeper clean. This is because the cuticles have been opened on the first shampoo. And, unless you have excess oil on the scalp caused by a hormonal imbalance, leave the scalp be. A healthy, well-oiled scalp means healthy hair.

Grab the conditioner but be sparing with this, too. Apply it from what I call the mid-lengths of your hair (half-way down your hair strand) to the ends and then use a comb to work the conditioner through. You can take the comb to the roots with a little of the residual conditioner on it during the second comb through – work it, Baby! This will help distribute the conditioner more evenly and get it to where it is needed. The important thing about conditioner is that it closes the cuticle of the hair, making it lie flat. This prevents tangling and gives your hair a shine.

Washing and conditioning this way will give you bouncy roots, a happy scalp, reduced hair loss and repaired, protected and moisturised ends. With a crowning glory like this, who knows what might happen?

Time To Declutter

Kat is neck deep in boxes and bubble wrap at the moment. In a couple of weeks, she is jetting off to sunny Qatar to live, so she is packing up her house, giving away junk and selling off things that are surplus to requirements. She is basically deserting us for a sunnier climate, and to live in a giant sandpit. Although from the pictures I have seen so far, it looks like a pretty funky sandpit!

I don't know if you have ever moved house, but it is a great way to get rid of the clutter from your life. Things that you store because you *might need them later'* become bin fodder. It's quite a cleansing process.

My current house is just big enough, and I'm pretty good at having a clear out now and again in order to leave plenty of space to live in. Although my booze cabinet is looking a bit full now because Kat has had to give away all her wines and spirits because she can't take them with her.

Shame!

Anyway, decluttering your life tends to make you feel good. It gives you a sense of achievement and sharpens your focus so that you can go forward. And you can make more room for the shopping that you're undoubtedly going to be bringing home!

Funnily enough, your hair needs decluttering now and again, too. The build up of pollution, oils and products (yes, I know some of you still use naughty products!) need to be cleansed away with a purpose-built clarifying shampoo.

It's a simple, small step but it makes a big difference. Come and test it for yourself.

Speak soon,
Terry xxx

P.S. The local council certainly love to cleanse the local environment. They are digging up the road outside the salon again. So far they've discovered no hidden treasure.

Soap For Tea

Talking about decluttering my house reminded me of when I used flat share with a guy called Tim. Tim is a pretty cool guy. He is a very talented hairdresser and when he lived here he had his own salon and a wild party lifestyle. There was always plenty going on when Tim was around. He has since moved to Australia (I feel sorry for the Australians, even as a Kiwi!), but the reason I am writing about him is that he was a bit of a hoarder. Or more to the point, he was a bit of a 'forgetter', particularly when it came to food. He would buy stuff, put it in the cupboard and then forget it was there.

One chilly winter's night, I decided to make a stew with dumplings. I rustled around in the cupboards and found a packet of suet, which, as disgusting as it sounds, is animal fat taken from around the kidneys, shredded and mixed with flour. It makes the most amazing dumplings.

So I get busy and make these dumplings. Everything smells good, the stew looks delicious and everyone is hungry.

First bite and OMG!

The dumplings taste like soap.

They are absolutely inedible.

Disaster.

I go and check the packet and lo and behold, the suet was *seven years* out of date!

It had been festering in our cupboard for almost a decade.

So, after we had ordered a take-away, we had a bit of a clear out.

The moral of this story? *Always check the dates.*

Speak soon,
Terry xxx

Going For A Tramp

I was in the salon last week chatting to a lovely Kiwi customer. The conversation went along the lines of:

Customer: *"I went for a tramp at the weekend."*

Me: *"Really? I miss going for a tramp. I love tramping."*

Now, any Kiwis reading this will know exactly what *'going for a tramp'* means, but I didn't realise that my harmless conversation could be misconstrued to the extent of causing concern.

Let me explain...

Gill, our Canadian receptionist, understands a tramp to be a down-on-his-luck, possibly homeless man with no teeth and a scraggy beard. When she heard us, she thought that we were literally going to commit violence. *'Going for a tramp'* and *'tramping'* sounded a bit dodgy to her.

And I think if I had said the same thing to Kat's five-year-old daughter, she would interpret *'going for a tramp'* as bouncing on a big rubber mat attached to springs.

Which led me to think about how important it is to use words in the right context. When we talk to you about how you would like your hair to look, we need to make sure that your understanding of 'big blow dry' is the same as ours. After 30 odd years I am pretty good at interpreting the context as well as the words, and so is my team.

Oh, I nearly forgot. When you say, *"I'm going for a tramp,"* to a Kiwi, it means, *"I am going for a long walk in the bush (or up the mountain)."* You would probably call it hiking.

Nothing dodgy about that *at all.*

Speak soon,
Terry xxx

 *Tip: Going short*

One of the things that I am really hot on is constant training and improvement for all my team. There is no such thing as knowing everything, and even though hairdressing is a lot about creativity, if you don't have the basics etched on to your brain so that they become second nature, creativity alone will get you nowhere. One of the things about hairdressing is that it is repetitive and training requires a lot of hands on experience and practice. I am a great believer in training competitions so that the team can pit themselves against each other to come up with something new, unique or classic with the skills they have. Then they can learn from it by being critiqued by an independent judge. And it's not as simple as just coming up with something on the day. They spend a couple of weeks producing a mood board of the theme they are going for, practising the techniques and sourcing models before coming up with the finished product in a very tight time frame on the night. It's exhausting for all but the benefits are huge. They come away with more confidence and some new skills. That benefit is then passed on to you as they are able to take those skills and techniques to their everyday work. The competition we had recently was for a short haircut and Gleb won with a very simple but beautiful style.

So, if you do have a short haircut, how do you look after it? People often forget that it is sometimes harder to maintain a short cut than a long one.

Here are 4 simple tips:

1. Get regular trims

This seems pretty obvious, but it's the most crucial thing to remember. Short hair looks great when the shape is maintained. This means regular trips to the salon, even more than if you had longer hair. Short hairstyles need to be cut every four to five weeks in order to maintain their shape, style and freshness.

2. Develop a healthy hair routine

Shorter hair needs its own set of products. Use products prescribed for your unique hair type. A good shampoo and conditioning routine is important because even though the hair is short, it still needs to be kept healthy and shiny. Shampoo and condition your hair as usual, and yes, use a weekly treatment designed for your hair type. This will prevent dry hair and frizz

3. Treat your scalp

To keep your scalp in top condition, and to encourage healthy hair growth, it needs to be treated the same way as the skin on your face. Just as dead skin and pollution can build up on your face blocking your pores, your scalp can get weighed down, too. Build-up on your scalp can mean flakes, dryness and irritation. Think about adding a clarifying shampoo to your hair care routine. This shampoo is great, as it serves as a facial for the hair and stimulates the scalp.

4. Avoid product overload

If you've been relying on an array of styling products to keep your strands in shape, it might be time to take a break or at least be choosier with what you use. Certain hair care products can do more harm than good in the long run. Gels and waxes can make your hair look greasy. This is okay if you are going for the 80's 'wet look', but Darling, that was in the 80s. Overuse of these types of products can clog hair cuticles and make hair look dull, oily and lifeless.

No Bombing!

Mr. Tom Daley, the fabulous Olympic athlete, has been in the press for what I think are all the wrong reasons this week: (a) because he *'came out'* as gay and (b) because he is allegedly dating a guy 20 years his senior.

In his words: *"Still Tom. Still diving. Going for gold in 2016. What I am or who I date shouldn't matter."*

Truth.

Who you are and what you do is nobody else's business, as long as you aren't harming another individual.

Tom is an extremely talented athlete, and he has inspired many people to take up sport. Yes, he looks hot in a pair of Speedos, but he is also an ambassador for British sport, a supporter of charities and a genuinely nice guy.

As you know, I love swimming (and yeah, I am sure I look hot in Speedos too!), so I was pretty excited when I won a pool sign that was signed by Tom himself. This was in an auction to support the charity *Leukaemia CARE*. The sign depicts a person *'bombing'* (when you dive in butt first to make a huge splash – great fun) with a strike through it (think Ghostbusters), and it says: *'No Bombing!'*.

You will never bomb as long as you stay true to yourself and don't worry about what others think about you.

The same message applies for your hair.

If you like it, you feel good.

If you feel good, you act more confidently.

When you are confident people comment and compliment.

So, how you want your hair is *your* choice.

You decide.

Easy peasy.

Speak soon,
Terry xxx

P.S. The first lot of shipping has been collected from Kat's house to head off to Qatar today. She says that she has spent a lovely morning watching a fit young bloke pack boxes, all the while pretending to work. Wish I could've been there! Ah well, I'll have to keep on dreaming. Back to reality…why don't you join me?

The Best Fitting Shoes

Last week all My Girls, (different from My Queens – my stylists who are, funnily enough, all male) got together to have a training session on head massage, shampooing and reception. I treated them to a makeover from my fabulous friend Chris who is a magician with an eye-shadow brush. Then we had a home cooked meal (prepared by moi) and gossiped.

See, it's good to get together now and again so that we all know what we are doing. Our communication needs to be seamless, particularly as the reception and assistant team are part-time and have to ensure that everything is covered in the cross over. They are vital for making sure that everything is running smoothly in the salon so that My Queens can come in and concentrate on being creative and technically excellent.

Tina is our resident giggler, but sadly she is leaving us at Christmas to study beauty therapy. **Gill** is our Canadian Queen Receptionist, and you can tell that she was once a model. She has some fab photos from her modelling career in the 80s, but I'm glad her hairstyle has been updated since then.

Tendai deals with everything technical, as well as manning reception and keeping the salon stocked up with products and refreshments. Nothing fazes her, not even the gypsies who come in and try to steal our charity box. **Kasia** has been with us for a couple of weeks now and is already fantastic at shampooing, applying colour, blow drying and keeping Gleb in his place. **Alisha** starts with us in January, so we are yet to find out about her personality, but what we have learnt so far is that she is very creative, which is a good start in a salon.

Oh, and **Kat**, *'The Queen of Everything'*, is my business partner and if it wasn't for her we wouldn't even have a bank account set up yet (even after five years).

Anyway, we have a big mix of personalities and, as Gill told a client the other day, *"it's like finding the best shoe fit."* One size does not fit all.

But, as big as the mix is, the one thing that my team is focused on is making life easy for you.

That's one less hassle for you to worry about.

Speak soon,
Terry xxx

P.S. Kat has five more days before she jets off to Doha. She tells me that her house looks like her cupboards have exploded and random clothes are mixed with umbrellas, clocks, paintings, toys...I'm sure you get the picture. I think she will be relieved when the movers come and take over. I don't think that packing is one of her strong points!

Is Yours Round Or Square?

My mum makes a square one.

My mother-in-law makes a square one.

My ex-wife makes a square one, which is dense and heavy.

I make a round one.

I'm not sure what you are thinking right now, but I'm talking about Christmas cakes!

I didn't know until recently that there is so much etiquette surrounding the shape of a Christmas cake. I discovered that the traditional shape is square and it is actually wedding cakes that are round (shaped after the spire of London's famous St Bride's Church, Fleet Street).

Well, I suppose I have always been a bit different.

Round peg, square hole and all that.

My Christmas cakes are legendary now, whatever their shape, and a huge hit in the salon during the festive season. In fact, Sam, one of my gorgeous Kiwi clients, emailed me especially to advise me that her appointment was on a certain day and at a certain time, and to make sure that some cake was put aside for her. She was afraid she would miss out. Actually, Sam is getting married at the end of this month in New

Zealand. While I know her highlights look fabulous (we did them before she left), I wonder if her wedding cake will be round or square?

Gotta go, can smell cake burning!

Speak soon,
Terry xxx

P.S. An update from Doha. Kat's living room is big enough to swing a five-year-old around, and around, and around, and around in. Sounds like she needs some furniture, or a carousel…a round one.

There Will Be Fireworks!

I promised some of you that I would tell you about New Year's Eve six years ago when Kat went into labour with her daughter, Heléna.

Don't worry, it's not going to be a gory birth story, just a little drama.

So, Kat had just moved to the East End of London (as you do when you are eight months pregnant and can't lift boxes), but she was still booked into St Thomas' Hospital in Lambeth to have Heléna. She didn't want to change as she knew all the midwives there and this was her first baby, so she was a bit anxious about the whole thing.

St Thomas' is a great big teaching hospital situated on the River Thames, right opposite the Houses of Parliament and just down the river from the London Eye. The birthing unit has a great view of all three landmarks. It is also in a prime location to view the New Year's Eve fireworks, which are lit from a barge in the middle of the river near the London Eye (more on that later).

Heléna's due date was December 23rd. One thing I know about babies, having two daughters myself, is that they rarely arrive with they are meant to, and this was the case with Heléna. It was a cold winter and I think she wanted to stay put! However, as all good things must come to an end, Kat went into labour on the morning of New Year's Eve. As her contractions quickened, Kat, her husband Kelvin, her mum and the midwife decided it was time to head to the hospital. By this time it was 11pm and what should have been a 15-minute journey in the car turned into an hour-long nightmare ride.

Remember where the hospital is situated?

Well, they put up roadblocks all around the hospital so that the hordes of revellers could walk along the roads to see the fireworks.

After Kelvin got lost in the back roads of Bermondsey (not something I would ever recommend), he had to get the police to lift the cordon before driving slowly through the crowds while Kat was screaming in the back seat.

Eventually, they reached the hospital and maternity ward just in time for the fireworks to be seen from the best viewing spot in town.

I bet you can't imagine what Kat said to Kelvin when he said, *"Oh, wow, just look at the fireworks!"*

Speak soon,
Terry xxx

Tip: Pregnancy and hair loss

Kath is a client that I have known for more than a decade. A few years ago, after giving birth, she noticed that her lush, dark brown hair was coming out in clumps in the shower as she washed it. For a while, there wasn't much of a noticeable difference, but over time her hair started to look lank. Then bald patches appeared along her hairline. To be honest, she looked like a dog with mange, well, maybe not that dramatic, but you get the picture. So, as well as having to cope with the demands of a new baby, the change in her body and the constant exhaustion, she also had to contend with a dip in self-esteem due to insecurities about her hair.

What the birth classes don't tell you is that *hormones* can make your hair fabulous, and also wreak havoc on it.

That old chestnut of *'everyone will experience something different'* also applies. Some women don't experience such drastic hair loss, some will experience more, some will notice a change in the condition of their hair and some may end up with coarse, curly hair instead of their original straight, fine hair.

Hormones...

What a curse!

BUT...

There are things that you can do to help get your hair back to its optimal condition.

Eat well. See my tips on eating your way to healthy hair on page 104.

Use a gentle shampoo and conditioner. Your scalp may be extra-sensitive at this time.

Try a cut that hides the bulk of the loss.

Consider a change of colour. Lighter colours can make hair look thicker. Our semi-permanent watercolours are safe to use during pregnancy and breastfeeding, and they give the hair a wonderful shine.

Try a hair loss/hair growth formula to minimise the loss and speed up new growth.

Sorry For The Rain

I just want to apologise for all the bad weather at the moment. I hear that it's all my fault.

Or so says David Silvester, the *UKIP* (UK Independence Party, a right-wing political party for those of you outside the UK) councillor from Henley-on-Thames, Oxfordshire. He said in a letter to his local paper: *"The scriptures make it abundantly clear that a Christian nation that abandons its faith and acts contrary to the Gospel (and in naked breach of a coronation oath) will be beset by natural disasters such as storms, disease, pestilence and war."*

He added: *"I wrote to David Cameron in April 2012 to warn him that disasters would accompany the passage of his same-sex marriage bill.*

"But he went ahead despite a 600,000 signature petition by concerned Christians and more than half of his own parliamentary party saying that he should not do so.

"It is his fault that large swathes of the nation have been afflicted by storms and floods."

Well, you can't beat stupid and this man seems to have it in spades. Not only does this opinion defy logic, it's just this type of attitude that led to the deaths of many women (and men) in the 16th, 17th and early 18th Centuries. When crops failed, so called witches, sorcerers and prophets were blamed, and often hanged for their *'crimes'*.

As there are four of us *'gays in the village'* working in the salon, I am surprised that you can make it through the door with all the weather and turbulence outside. Maybe I should go to some drought-ravaged country to bring them some relief?

The latest is that Mr. Silvester has been forced to step down from his role.

The thing is, he will still have his opinion, and I will still be gay. What he thinks does not worry me, in fact, I don't think of him at all!

Speak soon,
Terry xxx

Da Daah Da Daah Da, Daah Daa

Yesterday I pretended I was Bond, James Bond.

Well, in my head anyway.

You see, I have a friend who works in the Foreign Office and does all sorts of secret stuff - too secret to tell a hairdresser (you know how we like to gossip, lol).

Anyway, he invited me to join him for lunch in the staff canteen (doesn't sound so glamorous now, does it?). I know it wasn't the offices of MI6, otherwise I would have been singing the James Bond theme tune as I walked through the doors, but the Foreign Office and MI6 have a special relationship, I believe.

It was a nice day out, different from what I am used to, and definitely a step up from our back room in the salon for lunch!

I got to have a little tour and saw the door of 10 Downing Street from where the journalists stand.

Unfortunately, Mr. Cameron delayed his appearance for me, but I had to leave. Sorry David, maybe next time.

I am just a small town Kiwi boy and I get these *'pinch me'* moments now and again when I get to do cool stuff like this.

And I never take it for granted.

It's all part of taking every opportunity that comes your way.

Speak soon,
Terry xxx

P.S. Kat is getting to grips with her weekends now being on a Friday and Saturday in Qatar, as that's the way they roll in the Middle East. It's apparently an uncomfortable feeling having Friday off after working for so many years on this day. I would think that going to work on a Sunday would feel even more strange. I guess it's what we get used to. So while she lazes about on her private beach (not at all jealous), we will sort out your appointments for you.

Somebody's Watching You

A while ago, I was approached by a salesman who wanted to sell me a camera security system for the salon. Initially, I thought he was talking about a camera that would sit above the shop door outside to record any suspicious behaviour and act as a deterrent for anyone trying to enter or damage the property.

I was *wrong*.

What he was really selling was a camera that would sit inside the salon above the till and record when each staff member arrived at work, and what they did all day. And the hook was that I could sit in the comfort of my home (or in fact, anywhere in the world) and watch them while they worked.

Apart from the fact that I have better things to do with my time than watch Gill or Tendai make a cup of tea, I did think that taking this kind of action would create quite a big rift between my team and me.

The thing is, I have employed people that I can trust, and I think that this is such an important value, on both sides. I need to be able to trust them to do the best job possible, and they need to be able trust me to provide an environment where they can. Admittedly, I have made some mistakes with a few former staff members, but they generally show their true colours fairly quickly, and I don't need a camera for that.

I can't always be in the salon so trust plays a big part in the relationship that I have with my team. If I can't trust them, they would be no good to you. Trust plays a huge part for you, too. You have to trust your stylist to interpret your hopes and dreams for your hair and give you the best result.

I turned down the guy down with the cameras. He was quite disappointed and couldn't see why I thought it was a really bad idea. I think he thought I was a bit nuts when I laughed at him.

I didn't think about it then, but I guess if I had taken him up on the offer, I'd have had to tell you that you were on Candid Camera each time you came to the salon. Well, there are no worries there as you are not, so feel free to come incognito and test out my trustworthy team.

Speak soon,
Terry xxx

The Eyes Have It!

The eyes are the windows to the soul, or so the saying goes. But do you ever stop to wonder how many eyes are watching you each day?

It's kind of a freaky concept, especially when you live in a large city like London. I guess this is why people become immune to the thought and carry on their business regardless. You only have to watch someone on the tube doing their full makeup in the morning to see how people can block out the rest of world while carrying out intimate acts.

They say that you are recorded an average of 70 times a day by CCTV cameras in London. Although that mostly happens while you are at work or shopping, you are also being watched at railway stations, in public parks and on the streets.

Cameras are mainly used to deter would be thieves, terrorists, hooligans and general law-breakers. But studies have shown that we act differently, even if we only know subconsciously that we are being watched. And it doesn't even have to be an actual person or a camera watching you. Posters of people's eyes with the message, *'We are watching you!'* have been successfully used to decrease thefts and littering.

So what's my point?

Well, if you are going to be watched and photographed that many times throughout your day, then you might as well look your best, right?

And where can you go for that to be done, I wonder?!

Speak soon,
Terry xxx

A Hidden Gem

I always get a bit excited when I find a hidden gem in London. This city is so big, and there are plenty of places to explore, but sometimes you end up tied to your own little patch because it is easy and life gets so busy sometimes. Anyway, this little gem I mentioned is a swimming pool in the heart of Soho.

As I've already mentioned, I am an avid swimmer. I'm not bad at it, and I can even do tumble turns. I've been doing this for so long that I go into autopilot when I'm in the pool. Actually, I find it a great place to think. If I'm simply ploughing up and down the lanes and not concentrating on my stroke or increasing my speed, my mind thinks of all sorts of things and I get very creative. At the end of my swims, I often wish I had a notebook so I could write my thoughts down.

But back to the pool.

When I arrived in London, some 15 odd years ago, someone mentioned a pool in Soho that was built in the 1930s and was situated at the end of the street I worked on. But it had closed down and I didn't get the chance to see it. Then, after undergoing a massive refurbishment, it reopened a couple of years ago. Last week, I went for a swim there. It's simply stunning. The pool is lined with marble and the roof is a vaulted skylight, which lets in loads of natural light.

If you ever get chance to dip your toes into the water at Marshall Street Baths, then do.

I have upped my swimming regime lately as I am off to Amsterdam to compete in the *GLAMM* competition. I have done this event before, but I still don't know what the acronym stands for. Someone reckons it's: *'Gay, Lesbian And Muscle Marys'*. Well, it's definitely Gay and Lesbian something!

The only problem I have with it is that the event separates the competitors into five year age categories, and I've gone up a category since I last swam. Getting old is not good for the ego, but I'm still hoping to kick the butts of those *Muscle Marys!*

Speak soon,
Terry xxx

P.S. After I had written all the above, I found out that it's *GLLAM*, not *GLAMM* and it stands for: *'Gay & Lesbian London Aquatic Meet'*. This is nowhere near as funny as Muscle Marys and would have made for a boring story!

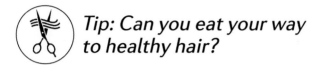

Tip: Can you eat your way to healthy hair?

Well, the old saying *"garbage in, garbage out"* is as true for your hair, skin and fingernails as it is for computer data entry.

It's also true that the condition of your hair can give a pretty good indication of how healthy you are, so here are some foods that you can add to your diet to give that hair a fighting chance.

Depending on how fast your hair grows, starting a hair-healthy diet today can improve the condition in as little as six months. **Add more of these six nutrient-rich foods** to your diet and tell me when you start to notice the results.

Chickpeas

In addition to providing zinc and folate (nutrients that promote hair health), chickpeas are a great vegetarian source of iron-rich protein, which is an important combination for hair growth and repair. Think hummus!

Skinless chicken

Skinless chicken breast is another healthy source of protein, and it's rich in the B vitamins - folate, B6 and B12 - that maintain healthy hair. These vitamins play an important role in the creation of red blood cells, which carry oxygen and nutrients to all the body's cells, including those of the scalp, follicles and growing hair. When the body is deprived of B vitamins, the cells can starve, causing shedding, slow growth or weak strands that are prone to breaking.

Lentils

Lentils are especially high in both folate and iron, which are two powerful nutrients that nourish your hair. Folate is a B vitamin that aids the creation of red blood cells. Iron helps those blood cells carry oxygen and nutrients to all the body's cells.

Strawberries

These are my favourite and they are a better source of vitamin C than oranges. Truth. And you don't have to peel them. Vitamin C does the job of promoting the health of collagen. Hate split ends? There is no cure for them but you can help prevent them as even a minor vitamin C deficiency can lead to dry hair that splits and breaks easily.

Swiss shard

I didn't even know what this was until recently! But it appears that I have been eating it in my exotic salads (when I was growing up in New Zealand, a salad consisted of Iceberg lettuce, a few tomatoes and some cucumber).

Swiss shard is a particularly rich source of biotin, which is a B vitamin essential for hair growth and overall scalp health.

Kale

Not just a pretty bunch of green to decorate fishmongers' cabinets. This beastie is packed with beta-carotene, which we convert into vitamin A. It's necessary for all cell growth and renewal and skimping on it can lead to dull, lifeless hair. You can sauté a bunch or two with a little olive oil and garlic, or try this delicious recipe for crispy kale chips:

Cut or tear fresh kale into pieces, place in a single layer on a baking sheet, mist with oil spray and bake at 200C (400F, Gas Mark 6) for about 10 minutes.

Hiding Behind The Paintwork

Why do kids love face-painting so much?

It's usually the most popular stall at a school fete, fayre or party and there always seems to be queues of kids waiting patiently to get colour applied to their faces, while peering over shoulders to see what face the lucky one in the chair is getting.

I'm guessing that it's because kids just love role-play and have great imaginations. When they are behind that paint they become someone else, whether that is a buttlerfly, a tiger or Spiderman. For the time that the paint is on their face (and before it gets smeared on to clothes and soft furnishings), they get to act like something fantastical.

I don't think that changes when you reach adulthood, either.

I've been known to paint my face up for a party on more than one occasion. Man, if you know me at all you'll know that I love makeup, even on a day-to-day basis. Maybe I was repressed as a kid – there was no such thing as a party entertainer or a face-painter in my day!

Whatever the reason, when you make a change to your appearance you act in a different way. You may find yourself becoming more confident and sexy. It's how actors do it, so it's not that hard! What's stopping you from making a change now?

Speak soon,
Terry xxx

P.S. Kat has been in Doha for nearly a month now and has to get her visa extended until her residence permit is processed. There are two ways that she can do this. Go down to the immigration office and wait for hours, fill in the correct forms, wear the right clothes and talk to the right people, or, alternatively, fly to Dubai for the weekend (and maybe do some shopping) and get a new visa on her return. Hmmmmm. What to do?

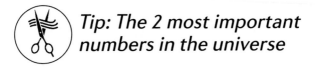

Tip: The 2 most important numbers in the universe

What would you say if I could free up more of your day so that you had more time for yourself and your hair care? Do you want to abandon the feeling that getting your hair in good condition is a luxury that you can't afford time wise?

It's no exaggeration to say that if you ignore just about everything else I say entirely and invest your time and energy into making what I'm about to share with you an almost religious observance in your life, then you and your hair will still be transformed beyond anything you imagined possible.

So, I am going to introduce you to a pretty cool dead guy called *Vilfredo*.

Vilfredo was an economist.

Stay with me now.

He discovered something that I think is amazing.

I am talking about *Vilfredo Pareto*, who, in his studies of the disparity of wealth in society, unwittingly stumbled upon what we now know as the *Pareto Principle*, or the *80/20 rule*.

In short, it means that in any system, the majority of the

effects come from a small number of causes. In Vilfredo's case, he found out that 80% of the land in Italy was owned by just 20% of the people. He then developed the principle by observing that 20% of the pea pods in his garden contained 80% of the peas.

This relationship holds true *all over the place*.

* In software, just 20% of the functions are used 80% of the time.

* 20% of your clothes get worn 80% of the time.

* Just 20% of your carpets get 80% of the wear.

* 80% of the people live in 20% of the towns.

* 80% of people die of just 20% of the most common causes.

* 80% of crime is caused by just 20% of the criminals.

* 80% of the time my bike gets stolen comes from the 20% of the time I leave it unlocked.

Truth.

* 80% of all your results come from just 20% of your work.

* 80% of the benefit from your hair products comes from just 20% of those products.

And so on...

The numbers aren't always exactly 80/20 and they don't have to add up to 100, so you might find they're 99/1, 75/20, and so on.

The point is, wherever you look in the universe, the principle holds: the overwhelming majority of effects come from a small number of causes.

The 80/20 rule underpins much of what I am planning to show you in the quest to get beautiful, easy-to-manage hair. These relationships do exist in your everyday life. You will find that by focusing your time and energy on the small number of things that give you the greater part of your results, you can cut out all the things that are getting in the way of your goals.

Excited?

Bet you never expected a lecture like that from a hairdresser! Well, we are a bit different at Hair Organics and it's not all about us, it's about you. Giving you back your time to do the things that are more important to you. More on that later (page 234) , when I can give you back a whole day a week to do whatever you please.

Getting Fitter To Enjoy It More

So, the *GLLAM* (*Gay and Lesbian, London Aquatic Meet*) weekend in Amsterdam has been and gone. Competitors were there from all over Europe; only about five of us were from the UK. It was a great event, really well organised and we had a great party on the Saturday night (truly I was there only for the swimming!).

I've come away with a few medals - one silver and two bronze - but the whole system of scoring is a bit beyond me. First, you submit a time that you think you can swim the stroke and distance in, say 1min, 25secs for the 100m freestyle (you're right, I'm no Michael Phelps), then you swim with all the competitors who have entered that time, regardless of their ages. The top placing swimmers go through to the next round, and the races get faster and faster until you die from lactic acid build up.

Truth.

Anyway, after all that, a whizzy-do computer calculates the times and separates out all the age groups and bingo, there's your medal!

Attending the meet made me realise that I need to get more practice in before I compete again. My times were pretty good at the start of the day, but I was fading fast by the end and it was just a matter of completing the distance. This goes to show that I need to increase my fitness to be able to enjoy the swimming more, and to kick more butt!

And the only way to do that is by repetition; getting out in the morning, even when no one else is around and it's dark, cold and raining, and even when my body and brain is screaming at me not to.

It's also how I am training my team in the salon. I'm doing some intensive repetitive work with them, making them get it right each and every time: no mistakes, no short cuts, just a perfect service, guaranteed.

Speak soon,
Terry xxx

P.S. I've just heard from Kat that her shipment of household goods has finally arrived in Doha and should be with her tomorrow. She is delighted that she will have sofas to sit on now instead of a picnic rug on the tiled floor in the living room. It's the small things!

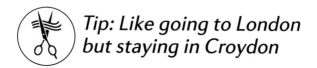 *Tip: Like going to London but staying in Croydon*

I had a lesson in *false economy* last weekend (and that's as cerebral as I'll get here). I needed to book somewhere to stay for the aforementioned *GLLAM* event. So, as you do, I got on the internet to look for a cheap room and found something that I thought looked quite nice. It only cost 175 euros for two nights. I was aware that some of my fellow competitors were staying at city centre hotels for 225 euros per night, but I thought what I had found would do me.

I liked the look of the room (it was an aparthotel), and it was only a 20-minute tram ride from the pool, but it turned out to be *two overground train rides away,* which meant it was a lot further out than I thought. This distance was made even more apparent by the 30 euro taxi ride that I took when I decided it was too difficult to figure out the trains on the first day.

To make matters worse, nothing worked in the room. One of the Dutch swimmers said: *"What are you staying there for? It's like going to London and staying in Croydon."*

Ouch.

So in reality, I spent *more time* and *money* getting to and from the venue and I should have just gone for something more central and convenient, even if it *did appear more expensive initially.*

This reminds me of a new client that came to the salon the other day. She said: *"I did my hair colour at home because I can't afford to come to the salon."* Well, yes, I thought. A box of chemicals was probably cheaper at the chemist or the supermarket, but now your hair is a nuclear shade of orange, is damaged beyond repair at the ends and you have stripes at the back where you couldn't quite reach.

However, it was great that the client had had the sense to come in and get her hair fixed, but she could have saved herself a *lot of time* and *money* by **having it done by an expert in the first place.** Her colour would have been the right shade, her hair would still be attached to her head and her dye would last longer because the condition of the hair would be better.

Rant over.

So, if you were thinking about DIY, resist the temptation and come and see me instead!

P.S. I am also reminded of one of Kat's favourite sayings when she is trying to persuade me to do something that I think is uncomfortable: *"Short-term pain for long-term gain."* Except coming to see us is never painful!

Resembling Maggie Thatcher

Kat, *'The Queen of Everything'*, is back in London for a couple of weeks. She jumped off the plane on Saturday morning at 6.30am and came straight to see us at the salon. After three months in the desert, she was desperate to give her hair a bit of colour, a treatment and a trim.

And of course, she marched in and started bossing everyone about. That's why we love her; she keeps us focused (her words). But she did say that it was great to be back amid the buzz and the vibe of the salon, especially on a busy Saturday. This is something she misses where she currently lives. She says that when she is in the salon it's like being in a club where everybody knows you. You can be yourself and it doesn't matter if you look ridiculous with your hair foils in. There is much gossip, laughter and chatting and, at the end of the process, you come out feeling fantastic.

Saturdays in the salon aren't what they used to be, though. There is more interaction between stylists and their clients and services can take longer. Back in the day, I used to do a shampoo and set in ten minutes and then dress out the hair in five minutes - after it had dried under the hood. My clients would be in and out in 30 minutes and looking like Maggie Thatcher.

This Saturday, the salon was alive with chatting, blow dryers and music. We were all busy doing our thing when we suddenly had one of those silences. All we could hear was a really bad rendition of the song, *MacArthur Park* (you know the one, it has that line in it which goes, *"Someone left the cake out in the rain."*). Everyone in the salon promptly erupted with laughter.

And there it was.

The shared experience when you are in a group and you all appreciate the same thing at the same time. It gives you that smug feeling of belonging to something that you can't share with anyone else because they weren't there in that moment. It's a powerful feeling, and gives you a buzz to carry you through the day.

And you just thought the salon was a place to get a haircut!

Speak soon,
Terry xxx

P.S. As soon as Kat was done, she rushed back to the airport to jet off to Ireland for a conference. The weather conditions couldn't have been more contrasting. She went from blue skies and sun in the desert, to bright, chilly London and then to miserable grey skies, gale force winds and rain in southern Ireland. Ah well, there's always a glass of red wine by the fire to look forward to. Kat can't do that in Doha! She can't get a decent salon in Doha either, but you can.

Do You Remember Your First Time?

I have just seen a picture of Kat's daughter, Heléna, who has lost her first tooth. Kat is really disappointed that she wasn't there in Doha to actually see it (apparently there was much excitement, jumping up and down and cheering). She's over here in the UK at the moment, and it's another a little milestone that she has missed.

Someone commented that Heléna has got plenty more teeth to come out, so Kat won't miss all the fun.

But it's not the same is it?

Why is it that we attach so much emotion to doing things for the first time? The first time is usually not the most perfect. It's fumbling, clumsy, funny, painful, scary, exhilarating, frustrating, and many other things. It's not until we have done that thing many times that we become skilled at it. But I guess that is because we have actually done something for the first time. We have participated and been present.

As Woody Allen once said: *"80% of life is showing up."*

So, will you show up?

Speak soon,
Terry xxx

One Is Not Late For The Palace

Yesterday was royal day in the salon. Kat, *'The Queen of Everything'*, was in getting a blow dry, and a client, Louise, was getting her hair coloured and made beautiful, as she was off to Buckingham Palace for a very important meeting. We also had a true blue European princess in the salon too!

I really felt for Louise. It was her first time in the salon and she had got lost trying to find us. She was in a panic because she had a very tight schedule in which to get her hair looking beautiful, change into her formal clothes and have her makeup done.

One is not late for The Palace...

No one...

Never...

Ever!

The End.

So not only did she have the anxiety of attending a meeting at one of the most formal places on the planet, she also had the stress of finding a salon that she had never been to before, with the wrong address, and had to trust a new stylist to *'get it right'*.

It reminded me of one of the times I went to The Palace (yes, I've been more than once), and on the way there I realised that I had left my passport, which is required for security reasons, at the salon. We had just 15 minutes to get there and I swear that all the blood in my body drained out through my shoes. When I told the taxi driver he said, *"No worries mate, you can't be late for her indoors."* He then proceeded to race back through town like he was the lead, support and all extras in *The Fast and the Furious 1,2,3,4,5,6* and *7*. I felt like James Bond. Needless to say, I made it back to The Palace on time and was able to relax, but I have the horrors just thinking about it now.

We got Louise out of the salon on time, too. She was looking great and I hope her meeting went really well, too. She deserved it

Speak soon,
Terry xxx

P.S. You think I have forgotten about our third royal, don't you?! Well, I haven't, but I can't tell you. What I can say is that she is lovely and normal and, best of all, she was referred to us by a friend. You wouldn't even know she was royalty because she is so unaffected. The only way you would find out is if you were in the salon at the same time as her, and even then you probably wouldn't realise who she is.

A Famous Lump Of Ear Wax

Kat has been at a conference in Ireland and has come back all fired up with ideas to introduce to the salon. The whole team got together last Wednesday night to toss some ideas around. Some great things came out of it, so watch this space!

Before we started the meeting though, Kat told us about how she had sat next to a celebrity on the plane home from Cork. She got quite excited and a bit tongue-tied when he spoke to her. Why does that happen? Why are we so enamoured with people who are on TV or in the media? Surely they are just like you and me. Is it because we want to associate with successful people (and we connect celebrity with success), and are seen as successful ourselves by mere association?

Probably.

Anyway, this is how the story goes, in Kat's own words:

"After a productive few days at my conference, I got a bit excited when I boarded the plane to find I was sitting next to a well-known celebrity.

After a very short exchange he said I was very sweet. He then proceeded to poke his little finger in his ear and eat the earwax.

Ewwwwwww!

This just goes to show that celebrities are just human.

Some are not as nice as others, and some have gross habits, too!"

I have to admit that I am still a little bit in awe of celebrities, but having worked with so many, the novelty has worn off.

Speak soon,
Terry xxx

P.S. Kat and I are taking part in a photoshoot this afternoon so that we'll have some nice pictures for our PR campaigns. Kat won't need much fluffing, but as I am past 50 now, I might need a bit more time in *'makeup'*.

No Explanation Necessary

You know how sometimes you can *'just click'* with certain people?

There is this instant bond and often no words are necessary, because you just know that you are on the same page.

That's what it is like with Kat and me.

We have been friends for over 20 years now (yeah, we met in kindergarten), and have been business partners for nearly six of those. And we just get on. She does her thing and I do mine, but we are always on the same page, even if we disagree.

Which is why, when we had a little photoshoot of our own, it only took about 30 minutes (usually a shoot can go on all day). Admittedly, 25 of those minutes were taken up by me in front of the mirror making myself look fantastic, but we got some great shots to use in our PR and marketing bits and pieces.

The great thing is that when you have a friend like that, no matter where in the world you are, it's always easy to pick up where you left off. You totally *'get'* each other, no explanations necessary.

Speak soon,
Terry xxx

 *Tip: Colouring at home*

So, you go out and buy a bottle of dye from the chemist. If hairdressers do it, how hard can it be, right? (And you know the type that hairdressers are, don't you? They are the ones who didn't do well academically, had an endless stream of boyfriends and even more hair colours. I split my sides laughing every time I hear that stereotype.)

And as the dye goes on, you get a bit confident. This is not so bad, you tell yourself. But then you realise that you can't really see that well at the back, and you have emptied more on to the top of your head than the ends. You wonder if that will matter. And there is now dye on the white bathroom wall, and on the floor, and a smear is running down the back of your neck and you haven't really seen to it that the tops of your ears were covered…

You sit for the required time and then you go and wash the dye off in the shower. By now there are colour splatters everywhere and the shower is never going to look the same again, to say nothing of the towel.

But you are ready in anticipation because that shade on the box was exactly right, and the model's hair is so shiny and she looks so happy, successful, thin, gorgeous and wealthy and you bet she has a glamorous life jet-setting around the world, has fabulous friends and goes to great parties. You bet she looks great in anything too, and has a great wardrobe.

And then there is the big reveal as you blow dry your hair and move it around with your hands, pulling it away from your face and fluffing it forward again over your forehead, like you see them do in the salon. Then you pull it back from your face again and what's this – there are still some grey hairs there! How could this have happened?

And what is that dark patch? And what is that line there?

Oh My God!

Is that ORANGE?

If this all sounds familiar, then whom are you kidding? Is the knot of dread in the pit of your stomach when you have to go out in public like that worth the hassle?

Or would a relaxing hour in a salon be worth it to stop the pain?

I'm Having A Stroke

Four years ago, on a very busy Saturday in July, an older gentleman came bursting into the salon and announced, *"I'm having a stroke"*.

I had owned the salon for just over a year and was still getting used to all the different types of people who came through the door, aside from genuine customers. I've have had tourists asking for directions to Portobello Market (they have to donate coins into our charity box before we tell them it's down the road and around the corner), gypsy women who have physically taken the charity box out of the door with them after '*borrowing*' the toilet, nuns and priests collecting money for their own charities, and some people who would class as genuine charity cases themselves.

It doesn't matter who they are, they are all greeted with a smile and a *"How can I help?"*

Except for the guy having a stroke.

I don't know if you have ever had a moment when you just became paralysed and didn't know what to do, say, or where to turn? Well 99% of the people in the salon that day found themselves in that situation. Luckily Kat, *'The Queen of Everything'* (first aid trained and a nurse's daughter) came to the rescue and immediately called for an ambulance.

The paramedics arrived pretty quickly and the salon became animated again. You will be relieved to know the man wasn't actually having a stroke after all.

The sad thing was that the paramedics knew the man and said that we had definitely done the right thing calling them, though it was unusual to see him out of his normal geographic area.

You see, he was homeless and although he was semi cared for in a shelter, when he felt that it was all too much for him, he would feign the symptoms of a stroke. By doing this he could get the paramedics to come out, who were then obliged to take him to hospital where he would get a warm bed for a couple of days, some good food and treatment for whatever ills he did have, before being released.

What got me was that the man's, *"I'm having a stroke"* line was his dignified cry for help. He knew what he needed, but instead of asking for it outright, which would likely result in being told to move on, he figured that the best and fastest way to get help was to ask for something more urgent. And it got the result he wanted.

I learnt a lot about myself that day, and in the future I will not hesitate to call the emergency services if someone says that they are having a stroke. You just never know.

I also learnt that to get the results you want, you have to take action. No one is going to help you if you don't get out there and do something.

Don't wait until you are desperate and despondent. The best time to act is *now.*

Speak soon,
Terry xxx

P.S. I was speaking to Kat the other night about her experiences of driving in Doha. She said that she sees an accident every day, and that although driving is like dancing with a partner in Doha - you have to be in sync with each other's moves - it's the wildly flamboyant and the ones that *'want to dance their own steps'* who cause the accidents.

Even '1' Would Have Been A Crowd

I have been thinking about some of the big swimming events that I've been to over the years.

One of the biggest was when I was chosen to be in the England team for the Gay Games in Sydney 2002.

I was so excited to be taking part. Firstly, it was in my neck of the woods. Sure, Australia is not New Zealand, but it is in the right hemisphere and a closer time zone. Secondly, it was the first time that the Gay Games had been hosted in the southern hemisphere. Thirdly, the swim event was being held in the newish Olympic Aquatic venue that had hosted the Sydney 2000 Olympic Games. Last but not least, 14,000 lesbians, gay men, bisexuals, transgender and straight people (and thousands of their nearest and dearest from around the globe) would be attending the event.

Wow!

I thought that it would be a dream come true, not only because I would be swimming in an Olympic venue, representing a country, but also because of the thousands of people coming to watch. The Sydney Aquatic Centre seats 10,000 spectators. Imagine how excited I was!

Well, the day of the competition arrived and I fronted up to the pool and had a peak at the crowd. Great, I thought, there were about 3000 competitors, coaches and staff in the stand on one side of the pool. But something was wrong. As I glanced around the venue, I couldn't see a single spectator in the stands.

No one.

Nada.

Not a sausage.

Even one would have been a crowd.

And it stayed that way throughout my competition.

Such a disappointment!

Anyway, in the end I had a great time and really enjoyed the experience.

Next time, though, I'm rounding up my entourage and we will take over the stadium!

Speak soon,
Terry xxx

P.S. Kat has been a MotoGP widow for the last few days. Kelvin has been out each night watching guys on big bikes battle each other around a circuit in return for a podium place and a little gold trophy. Qatar is definitely the place for burning rubber and fossil fuels. Filling up a big SUV with petrol costs just £10 a fortnight. I can't see the attraction of motorsports myself, unless it involves lads in leathers. Although my preference would be lads in Speedos!

A Very Delicate Ankle

Someone asked me the other day why I don't compete in triathlons.

You see, I love swimming and get a thrill out of competing in the pool. I also love cycling and it is my transport of choice around London, whatever the weather. It's a great way to keep fit and save the fare on the Tube! It's also a great way to explore parts of London that you wouldn't normally see.

One of my favourite rides is along Regent's Canal, all the way out West and back again. Although it's not without its hazards. I regularly encounter narrow lanes under bridges, cyclists hurtling on to the towpath too quickly and dog walkers with their pets on extra-long leads.

Ouch!

But the reason I don't compete in triathlons is that I can't run to save myself.

This may be a gay cliché, but I have *soft ankles.*

If I run I inevitably turn one, which in turn wrecks my knees, which is turn wrecks my lower back, which in turn does my head in (and the heads of all of those around me).

So I remain an armchair supporter of triathlons.

It's a shame as the sport is enjoying a huge surge in growth, and there are more women between the ages of 30-49 taking it up than in any other age demographic. Which goes to show that it's not just for the youngsters. But I will stick to my swimming and cycling, and if anything new comes along that doesn't involve running, I'm in.

Speak soon,
Terry xxx

P.S. This has reminded me to tell you about my friend Jarred who competed in the gruelling New Zealand Coast to Coast competition, which involves running, cycling and kayaking, without being able to swim. He's got more brawn than brains!

Face Your Fears & Do It Anyway

Way back in 1992, I was support crew for Jarred when he competed in the Coast to Coast.

This is known globally as the ultimate sporting event and attracts around 800 competitors from around the world. I'd say that all of these people are a little bit nuts for wanting to attempt it.

Here's why:

The competition traverses the South Island of New Zealand, from Kumara Beach on the Tasman Sea, to Sumner Beach on the Pacific Ocean. Over either one or two days (individuals, two person or three person teams can compete over two days, individuals can opt to do it in one), competitors cycle 140kms (three stages of 55km, 15km and 70km), run 36km (including a 33km mountain stage that crosses the Southern Alps) and kayak 67kms of the Waimakariri River through the Grand Canyon of New Zealand, the Waimakariri Gorge.

Now New Zealand is a beautiful country, and the scenery in the South Island is pretty spectacular. But a day out taking part in the Coast to Coast is not.

It's physically and mentally grueling.

Most people train pretty hard leading up to the event and Jarred was no exception. He was a very competent runner and was good on the bike. He only had one fear.

Water.

He couldn't swim.

This didn't bode well for the kayaking section, given that falling out of a kayak requires you to have some basic swimming skills.

After all, your life kind of depends on it.

But this didn't stop Jarred. He just felt the fear and signed up to it anyway.

On the weekend of the event, I was in charge of setting up camp and being at the middle stage to meet Jarred after his run-cycle-run section. He was doing the event over two days and we had to camp overnight in the mountains. All was well until Mother Nature decided to intervene with the mother of all storms, which blew our tents down, raised the level of the rivers and flooded our campsite.

Happy days.

The rivers were so heavy and churning with flood water that the race organisers decided to cancel the kayaking section, which should have taken place on the morning of the second day.

This was a disappointment for most of the competitors.

But a result for Jarred.

Wearing a big smile on his face, he duly got on his bike and set the fastest time of any competitor for that section.

I think it was the relief of not having to face the water that gave him the extra boost.

I also think that to have that kind of determination when facing your fears is a pretty good way of getting through life. So, if you fear making a change, don't think, *"What if it goes wrong?"* Instead, think, *"What if it goes right?"*

Speak soon,
Terry xxx

P.S. Someone asked me what a '*Muscle Mary*' was the other day. Or rather, it should be, '*who is a Muscle Mary?*' I've run out of puff so I will have to tell you another time.

Muscling In On Mary

Back in the 1900s, when being gay wasn't healthy for you, i.e., it cost you your life or a lengthy time at Her Majesty's pleasure, the gay community came up with gay speak, or gay slang, to communicate in code. They could identify themselves without being identified, so to speak.

It was their secret language.

Some of those words are still around today, such as *'bear'* meaning a large and often hairy man, or *'twink'*, which denotes a young man.

And a *Muscle Mary* is a man who is effeminate but likes to work out at the gym, so is very muscular.

Not my type.

So there you go, secret revealed.

Speak soon,
Terry xxx

P.S. Kat has discovered (or rather has unleashed) her inner rally car driver! She told me that she drove on her own for the first time in Doha yesterday. She got her licence in the morning from the traffic department, which is also where you have to go to report an accident. There are numerous written-off vehicles languishing in the car park, which serve as a stark reminder of how mad the driving is over there. If that doesn't put you off, and you have nerves of steel, you get on the road and just *'go for it'*. The indicator becomes a decorative item and lane markings are only there to give road painters a job. Sounds like fun!

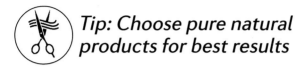 *Tip: Choose pure natural products for best results*

I have a friend who used to suffer from serious dandruff. Dandruff is commonly a problem for men. This is because excess testosterone can cause a surplus amount of sebum or natural scalp oil. Combine that with a speeding up of skin cell renewal (usually from a fungus), and the shedding of scalp skin builds up so much that clumps form and you get 'snow' on your shoulders, inevitably when you are wearing black.

Now at the time my friend, Daniel, was a young and handsome man and he had a way with the ladies. But he was terribly embarrassed by his dandruff and was losing his confidence.

Not good when you are known as the local lothario.

But instead of trying all sorts of different remedies, Daniel (he is a bit of a "I can do it better" type of guy) decided to get creative and took a book out from the library (remember those?) on the healing properties of flowers and herbs. He read that various flowers are good for conditioning your scalp and proceeded to strip his mother's garden of every single flower there was. He brewed them up in water and added his concoction to a large bottle of a Costco-type shampoo that his mum had bought for the family. You know, the ones you can buy in bulk. Warehouses stock them and you can purchase them for something ridiculous like £1 for five litres.

At the time, Daniel happened to be working as a hairdressing trainee in a large, well-known Central London salon. So he took some of his shampoo in with him to use on his customers.

The story goes that the salon owner loved the shampoo (it cleared up the eczema on his hands) and so did all the customers. So much so that the owner wanted Daniel to supply the salon with another five litres the following week.

But there was one slight problem.

There were no more flowers in the garden.

Okay, there were two slight problems.

No flowers and he hadn't told his mum about using up all the shampoo.

That's when Daniel Field became an innovator and inventor and pioneered organic and mineral hair care in the UK. He set up a laboratory in his parents' glasshouse at the bottom of the garden (which he subsequently blew up, but that's a story for another day) and got to work making his own unique shampoo.

He did ditch the wholesale shampoo as part of the formula, you will be pleased to hear, and now his products are as pure as possible. Which is why I love working with them.

What about the dandruff?

Gone.

Using his own concoction, Daniel managed to ditch the dandruff and pull the ladies.

Truth.

Like Having Your Brains Sucked Out

My friends and family complain that I am deaf because I can never hear what they are saying. They also often remark that I have my music up too loud, or that I haven't taken in some relevant information.

I refuse to believe them. After all, my reality is the actual reality.

But if I am really honest, the years of swimming have taken a toll on my ears and there is enough water in there to fill a small swimming pool. I don't know if you ever get water trapped inside your ear, but when I do I get this kind of scrunching, sloshing sound every time I move my head. Actually, it sounds a lot like Kat's squeaky voice so it's no wonder that I never hear what she is saying!

I have tried wearing earplugs when I swim, but the water still leaks through the cracks and if I am competing I can't hear the starter gun (which is more of a beep than a bang; Kat's squeak springs to mind again).

I have tried many remedies over the years to get rid of the water effectively, but the only thing that works for me now is getting my ears suctioned at the specialist's with a miniature vacuum cleaner. It kind of feels like you're having your brains sucked out of your ears, and I am sure the doctor sucks the cash out of my wallet using the same implement!

I've been reading about some of the weird things that end up in people's ears.

Dr. Simon Gane, founder of the *Clear Ear Clinic*, where I go to have my ears suctioned, once had to remove a tooth from a young female patient's ear. According to the doctor, the little girl wanted to keep it somewhere safe for the tooth fairy.

Too cute! A bit of a tight fit for the fairy to leave the money, though!

Speak soon,
Terry xxx

Simple & Beautiful

When I was a young and gorgeous apprentice, more young and gorgeous than I am now, my training consisted of late night practice on willing and not-so-willing models. Basically, these models were anyone or anything that had hair and didn't move around too much. The small town in New Zealand where I am from is quite isolated from the rest of the nation. This means that gaining access to all the big schools and colleges for hairdressing is pretty tough. In fact, back in the day, there probably wasn't any major college I could have gone to anyway. It was all 'learn on the job'.

One of the things that my boss, Judith, insisted on was that we all (from the senior staff through to the lowly juniors) competed in as many hairdressing competitions as possible. These competitions could be in our town, region or neighbouring regions. We would practise every night leading up to the competition and then we would all pile into Judith's van, negotiating many windy roads as we travelled to wherever the competition was.

It was a great way to learn quickly as the judges would pick apart our work and Judith would not accept a loss. We all had to come away with something. It was a life dedicated to hairdressing, and I loved it.

Nowadays, the profession has become more regulated and there are a million and one colleges with access to online learning and teaching support in salons. The competitions have sort of dried up, and only the big national ones are left.

But competition has some really great things going for it. It helps you focus, work to a time limit and see the quality of work that you are up against.

This is why I hold regular in house competitions for the team at *Hair Organics*. It keeps my stylists on their toes as well as current, fresh and creative so that they can offer you the very best.

We had one such competition recently for cutting short hair. It was interesting to see how each stylist interpreted the brief, and the winner was our token straight man, Gleb. His cut was simple but beautiful, a bit like his personality!

Speak soon,
Terry xxx

P.S. Kat has just had an X-ray and blood test for her application to get a residence permit for Qatar. She asked if she had to have a medical examination as indicated on the bottom of the form. She was told "no", as that was for *work* purposes only, so that the employer knows you are fit for work. Because she is a 'housewife', she only has to be fit for her husband. Ouch. I don't think that has gone down well!

Tip: You can't unboil an egg

'You can't unboil an egg'. I think that's how the saying goes.

In Kat's household, they have a particular family ritual that involves her hubby Kelvin cooking breakfast on a Saturday morning.

One particular Saturday he asked their daughter Heléna how she would like her eggs cooked.

"I want them round with a runny yolk so that I can dip my bread in them," she said.

So off Kelvin went to duly make breakfast. Once prepared, he presented the plates to everyone at the table.

Kat saw Heléna's face fall.

"Daddy, where are my eggs?" She asked.

"There on the table, Sweetheart, in the eggcups," Kelvin replied.

"But Daddy, YOU GOT IT WRONG! I wanted them to be round and runny, not boiled."

Poor Kelvin was confused.

"But I thought you wanted to dip your bread soldiers into a boiled egg?"

"No, I wanted them poached and runny!"

With that, Heléna picked up her plate and handed it back to Kelvin.

"I want you to go and unboil the eggs and make them poached," she demanded.

After that major disappointment, and a discussion about how Heléna could one day become a famous scientist who discovers how to unboil an egg, Kat and Kelvin persuaded her to eat breakfast (and also had a brief chat about the importance of manners).

Just like an unboiled egg, your hair is made up of protein. And just like the egg, once you change the protein structure it is very difficult to get it back to its original state.

Just A Minor Adjustment

Speaking of eggs, the following thought hit me: I am one of those strange people who cannot *stand* the smell of strong scent.

Most sorts of smells make me want to gag.

However, I love the smell of baking or cooking, which is good because I love to bake and cook. My favourites include the smell of a freshly baked banana cake or garlic frying in butter.

Delish.

No, it's more the manufactured smells that I can't stand, such as perfume, air freshener, incense or scented candles.

It really is a problem. I can't have air fresheners at home, and I don't use cologne or deodorant (lucky I don't sweat or smell – I hope!). They make me gag. It amuses my team, especially Gleb, our token straight man from Estonia. He's a fitness freak and is very masculine in his sweating. He told me that if he didn't use deodorant he would *"stink like pig!"*

I can't even let my partner wear cologne, and when I came home the other day and he was burning incense, my head nearly exploded.

I am not sure why it is, but it could be the result of having a nose job.

Now vanity is not particularly what I am known for, but only when you ask the right people. If you ask the people who know me well, they will tell you that I like to take care of my appearance, and I see nothing wrong with a little enhancement. It's like my lovely French client said the other day when we were tweaking her hair colour, *"Just a minor adjustment to achieve perfection."*

But having a nose job wasn't all vanity, I promise you...

Speak soon,
Terry xxx

P.S. I was going to reveal my new secret weapon in the fight for perfect hair today, but I've changed my mind. I thought I might make you wait a bit.

It will be worth it.

I promise.

A Bunch Of Lush Winos

I had the nose job done nearly 20 years ago.

Back then I had tiny sinus passages.

I'm sure you don't want to know the gory details, but every year without fail I would suffer with major sinus problems, which began around springtime.

This was beyond hay fever.

I lived in a small rural town in New Zealand called Blenheim, which is in the province of Marlborough. You may have heard of some little-known wine that comes from there – Marlborough Sauvignon Blanc. Well, to make wine you need vineyards, and the region is full of them. In fact, the vines ousted the sheep and the cherries, so you could be forgiven for thinking that the province is full of a bunch of lush winos, sitting back watching the grapes grow (not too far from the truth in my opinion).

Anyway, back to the vineyards.

In order for the grapes to grow fat and juicy you need to make sure that there are no bugs getting a free ride and eating the vines. So, rightly or wrongly, you need to spray. And spray they do. If the wind comes in from a certain direction you can often taste the chemicals in the air. That spray, combined with the high amount of pollen from all the trees, flowers and agriculture (beautiful place to live but deadly for hay fever sufferers), was lethal. Add to that my love affair with the swimming pool and chlorine, and my small sinuses. I often felt that my head was going to explode and would have to have a lie down on the floor of the back room.

I really needed to get it sorted out. My life was miserable.

So off I went to an ear, nose and throat specialist. He was a lovely American who had just arrived in New Zealand and also specialised in plastic surgery.

I knew that Americans know a thing or two about plastic surgery. At that time, Michael Jackson was single-handedly keeping the business afloat (well, maybe with the help of Elizabeth Taylor and Jocelyn Wildenstein, the *'Cat Lady'*).

Not that they were any great endorsement for the craft. But I wasn't thinking about that. All I wanted was for the pain to stop and to be able to breathe again. And I wanted it done by someone who could be trusted to know what they were doing.

Not too much to ask.

Was it?

Speak soon,
Terry xxx

Getting A *'Job Lot'*

Did you know that your sinuses are the size of a pin prick?

Well, 20 years ago, mine had grown over (ooh err).

As you know, I had been suffering terribly from sinus pain and headaches, so off I went to see the American ear, nose and throat specialist.

Dr. America suggested that he could fix the problem using a method, which, if I recounted it, would make you wince and squeeze your knees together in sympathy. I was all for it, but Dr. America also suggested (in that very easy American way of upselling - think McDonalds, *"would you like fries with that?"*), that perhaps I wasn't happy with the shape of my nose?

To be fair, it was quite crooked and had a large boney lump on the bridge. The thought of having it straightened and slimmed down a bit to make it look 'more balanced' appealed to me. Especially as he said it could be done at the same time as the sinus operation.

Why not?

Bring it on.

But wait, there was more.

Dr. America also had a good look at my face and suggested that maybe I was also unhappy with my ears?!

Do you know what a wingnut is? It's a special nut that has two ear-like pieces moulded on to the side so that you can turn it with your fingers instead of using a spanner.

Its appearance is not dissimilar to what my ears looked like at the time - they really stuck out of my head. I also used to have long hair and very tight curls. It was a bit of a full on style, but it did a brilliant job of hiding those ears.

Dr. America sold it well. I could have my sinuses fixed, be free of pain, have a new nose and have my ears pinned back so they would no longer be the butt of jokes like, *"Can you get alien signals with those antennae"*, etc.

I was in.

I went for the *'job lot'*.

The only problem now was the operation. I would have to have my nose broken and reconstructed and my ears sliced and diced at the same time. I knew it would be painful afterwards, but I was frankly so sick of the pain I was experiencing that this outweighed any apprehension.

Oh, if hindsight was foresight...

Speak soon,
Terry xxx

A Sniffer Dog Like Snoz

The day of the big op arrived. I was to have my sinuses bored out, my nose straightened and my ears pinned back. Tough me, I can take it. I was put to sleep and Dr. America did my nose first before rolling me over and doing one ear, then rolling me over again to do the other.

I proudly walked out of the clinic later that day swathed in bandages and sporting two massive black eyes covered by sunglasses that would rival Liz Taylor's.

The new Terry had arrived.

Well, nearly.

It took a week for all the swelling to go down.

And what a miserable week it was.

It was brutal. My face was black, and I had to try to sleep sitting up to avoid squashing my new ears. My wife at the time was not going to let me complain, though. She made some choice comments of empathetic support, such as, *"Your face is worth more than our house!"*

When the bruising and the swelling finally went away and the bandages came off, I went back to Dr. America for a checkup. He had a look inside my nose, grabbed some tweezers and proceeded to pull out a piece of rolled up plastic from one nostril. This just kept coming and coming and coming. It had been holding my nose open and I hadn't even realised it was there.

And OMG I could breathe again!

I remember that first breath so well. It was a deep through-the-nose-into-the-belly-breath, and it felt fantastic! No more struggling for air. The breath was crisp and clear and the smells were out-of-this-world intense.

Maybe too intense.

The op has left me with a sniffer dog like snoz, which means the slightest odour can cause great pleasure (such as baking or cooking), or do just the opposite and make my gag reflex raise its ugly head. But I consider it a very small price to pay for having my breath back without pain.

After that, I got all my hair cut off, bought some funky glasses and walked down the main street of Blenheim. At the time I was a big fish in a small pond. Everyone in town knew *'Terry the hairdresser'*. But not on that occasion. Not one person recognised me.

It felt great!

Then I got quite into investing in my looks and got my teeth done, too.

Vain? Not me!

Speak soon,
Terry xxx

Laying It All Bare

I have to admit that I was a bit embarrassed about sharing my personal story about having work done with you. I don't know why. A few people know, but it's not something that I talk about much.

Even though cosmetic surgery is so common, there is still a big taboo surrounding it. If you do it you are admitting that you are not perfect and that there is something wrong with you. And we have been led to believe as a society that vanity is wrong and we should accept the way things are.

It comes across a lot in the salon when we are colouring grey hair. Even down to the language we use. We say *'covering up'* or *'hiding'* the grey, like it is something secretive. But I say why not? If the technology exists for you to carry your entire music collection around in your bag wherever you go, then why not use the same type of innovation to make your hair more manageable, shiny or just have a change?

And that is the second reason for sharing my story with you. My first is that I wanted to lay myself bare and not hide anything. I am a real person that you can trust. I think it's important for you to know who you are dealing with, and I know that I am not to everyone's taste. That's good, because not everyone is right for *Hair Organics Notting Hill*, either.

I have been in the creative industry for over half my life, and I am a bit of a stickler for detail. Like my face, I can see where things can be enhanced to make something average look exceptional. You may have been born with it, or grown into it, but you don't need to stay that way.

Things can change.

Speak soon,
Terry xxx

Dishing Out Hope

I've had a number of emails over the last week regarding my cosmetic surgery. All of them were very nice and the senders all said how fabulous I look. This was very gratifying. Who doesn't love to get fan mail?

But I have been thinking about the process I went through, and my feelings at the time. I have come to the conclusion that it wasn't only about the physical act of face-changing surgery. There was something more intangible going on that was even more compelling.

What Dr. America was offering me was the hope that my problem could be solved. I anticipated that I would be free from pain and would be able to breathe properly and go about my daily tasks with greater efficiency. I would be better looking, more successful and happier.

Did it work?

Of course it did.

Firstly, this was because Dr. America is good at his job.

But most importantly, it worked because I believed it would.

Hope is something we dish out in the salon on a daily basis. And you thought that we just did haircuts!

Speak soon,
Terry xxx

A Recurring White Mouse

I experienced a phenomenon yesterday. I didn't know what it was called until I Googled it later, but it went like this.

Two days ago I was thinking about ANZAC Day, which is on April 25th. ANZAC Day is a national day of remembrance in Australian and New Zealand for all those who served and died in World War I and World War II (and any subsequent wars and battles).

In New Zealand, there is a dawn parade. Each town turns out its veterans to march down to the cenotaph and lay wreaths in honour of those young lives lost. Then it's a day off for the nation and everyone heads to the pub.

Anyway, as I was thinking about ANZAC Day and Kiwi traditions, my mind wandered to a famous relative of mine who was very influential in WWII. Her name was Nancy Wake, but she was also known as the *White Mouse.*

When she died, aged 98, the Daily Mail gushed: *'Blisteringly sexy, she killed Nazis with her bare hands.'*

Nancy, who was married to a Frenchman, played a vital part in helping more than a thousand escaped PoWs and shot down Allied airmen escape from occupied France. Dubbed the White Mouse for her elusiveness, she was number one on the Gestapo's most wanted list. Once, when her parachute got caught in a tree, her local agent said he hoped all trees could bear such beautiful fruit. She replied, *"Don't give me that French shit."*

She wrote her autobiography before she died and was a bit of a character by her own account. Not much fazed her, she liked a drink and she also liked to have her nails done, her hair styled and her lipstick on, even when she was in the field.

I wish I had met her, she sounded awesome. Not least because she was related through my grandmother – we were second cousins or something.

I am sure her attitude must have rubbed off on me down the line. I never go into the field without my lipstick on either!

Speak soon,
Terry xxx

P.S. I will tell you the name and a bit about the phenomenon later. Unless it pops up for you before then...

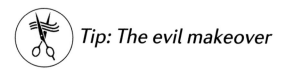 *Tip: The evil makeover*

Why are makeovers so popular?

Doing some research about these, I was amazed about how much negative press there is about having a makeover. The articles say that women are being forced into being something they are not and that they should just be themselves. They reckon that society shouldn't focus on what a person looks like and that you should be accepted for who and what you are. But what if who and what you are is someone who is painfully shy and self-conscious about your looks? You know that this is holding you back and you want to change all that.

There are a number of things that you can do to change your belief system and thought processes, but one of the quickest ways to get a *'fake'* boost to self-esteem is to change the way you look, which then converts to how you feel about yourself on the inside, which influences how you act.

This leads to a more confident approach and creates a positive cycle of cause and effect.

Where's the harm in that?

The argument is that society shouldn't dictate how you look and that beauty should come from within rather than being enhanced, but that doesn't help when you are not happy with how you look and this is creating stress.

Weather you feel sexy in jeans and a T-shirt or a strapless black thing, dressing up is always fun and can make you feel more confident. It is important for a woman to feel that giddy, 'I am sexy' feeling sometimes, and it can be an uplifting thing to get some flattering unsolicited attention.

So once you've had a makeover, you want to work your look.

After years of working with models on photoshoots, here are some tips for you to look good in photos:

1. Show your *'good'* side. To find yours, hold a piece of paper vertically over one side of your face. Your better side is the one with more upturned features, for example, the corners of your eyes and lips.

2. Control your chin. When you pose, elongate your neck and push your forehead and chin forward a bit. It may feel awkward, but this position helps define your jawline and gives your face a more angular, lifted look.

3. To get a natural looking smile do not say cheese. A real smile forces the muscles under the eyes to contract. To make that happen, squint slightly with your lower lids, Clint Eastwood style, as you smile. And aim your gaze at the top of the camera lens, which will draw your eyes up and make them look brighter and bigger.

4. Angle your body slightly to avoid facing the camera full front on. Physically turn your body 30 degrees and then turn your head towards the shoulder closest to the camera.

5. Lastly, just before the photo is taken, take a deep breath and release it. You will look more relaxed and smile more naturally.

Voila!

Gorgeous you.

Popping Up All Over The Place

So, the other day I was thinking about my feisty relative, Nancy Wake, who gave the Gestapo the run around during the Second World War, put her life in danger and rescued thousands of PoWs, all while maintaining her lipstick and hairstyle.

Isn't it funny how when you are thinking about something or someone like that, the subject pops up elsewhere all of a sudden, too?

For me, this happened when I saw Nancy on a list of the 50 coolest Kiwis. It was a random post on a website, and she was in the top 10 (well, it figures as she is my cousin 50 times removed).

Freaky or what?

This is called *frequency illusion*, or the *Baader-Meinhof phenomenon*, which sounds much cooler.

These terms are used to describe the syndrome in which a concept or thing that you just found out about suddenly seems to crop up everywhere.

Professor Arnold Zwicky said that the syndrome is caused by two psychological processes.

The first, selective attention, kicks in when you're struck by a new word, thing or idea. After that, you unconsciously keep an eye out for it, thus finding it surprisingly often as a result. The second process, confirmation bias, reassures you that each sighting is further proof that this thing has gained overnight omnipresence.

It's everywhere!

The reason for this is that your brain likes patterns. It has a fantastic pattern recognition engine that is highly useful for learning. This also means that you are more likely to place a lot of importance on unremarkable events.

When you hear a word or name that you have just learned, it often feels like more than a mere coincidence. This is because Baader-Meinhof is amplified by the so-called recency effect - your brain likes things that have happened recently and gives them a higher ranking of importance (a bit like Google, then!). This increases the chances of you being more aware of the subject when you encounter it again in the near future.

It was like when Kat said she was moving to Qatar. I'd never heard of the country, and yet suddenly every man and his manicured poodle had been there, worked there or knew someone who was already there. And it was coming up in conversation all over the place.

So there you go, mystery solved.

Sorry if I have spoilt the fairy magic for you!

Speak soon,
Terry xxx

A Gypsy In America

Nathan is our resident Romanian gypsy. If you think of a Transylvanian, he's it: a bit kooky, passionate, intense, has a big personality, but is also a lot of laughs.

The question is: would you let him loose on the United States?

Well, Nathan has wanted to visit the States for a long time. I don't know why, but he loves travelling (aha, that must be his gypsy side). This is a great thing in my opinion. It's fantastic to explore new things, immerse yourself in different cultures and eat different foods. It makes you an altogether more interesting person.

But back to Nathan. As I was saying, he has been trying to visit the States for a while, but has been turned down for a visa twice.

His boyfriend is American and he wants to take Nathan for a tour of his neighbourhood (San Francisco to be exact). To have a holiday with your lover and see the sights that usually only locals see is a great opportunity.

The offer is so compelling that Nathan decided to brave the rigours of the American Embassy again to try and get that elusive visa. He got prepared with bank statements, rental agreements, employment contracts, his passport, photos, application forms, references, and even receipts for underwear.

Armed to the teeth with all these documents, he turned up to the meeting ready to try and convince the officer that he is a worthy character to holiday in the States. He knows the drill you see, having done it twice before. It's a long process of convincing them that he has the means to support himself and that he is not going to go begging on the streets of San Fran or steal anyone's wallet.

The officer was friendly enough and Nathan started his spiel. He went for earnest, passionate and pleading.

The officer stopped

"I just want to ask you three questions," he said.

"OK," Nathan replied.

"How long have you been in London?"

"Erm, six years."

"Are you married?"

"No."

"What are you going to the United States for?"

"Ah, a holiday."

"Fine," said the officer. *"I'll approve your visa. Is a 10 year one okay with you?"*

Of course Nathan said yes, and his feet haven't touched the ground since.

I thought it funny how it doesn't matter what hoops you have to jump through, the decision rests with a human, and that human makes decisions in arbitrary ways. What's acceptable to one is not to another, and sometimes you just have to keep trying until you get the answer you want.

Speak soon,
Terry xxx

P.S. If you are in San Francisco in late May and you see an attractive Romanian Gypsy with his hand out on a street corner, send him home. He's got work to do.

Tip: Grease is the word, baby!

The new hair trend for spring has been seen on the catwalks in New York

It's grease.

Dare you?

Are we that desperate to see something new that we are regressing to teenage angst, rioting hormones and over-active sebaceous glands?

No way!

Although it has reminded me to tell you that it is far better for us to work with unwashed hair when you come into the salon.

There are a couple of reasons for this:

1. The natural oil that your scalp produces protects the head from the colour we use on it. Even though our colours are the least harmful in the world, some of you can be extra-sensitive to some of the ingredients contained in them.

2. It's easier for us to handle. Washed hair tends to be softer and can slip through our foils when we are doing highlights, creating an uneven effect. If we are doing an upstyle, soft, washed hair is impossible to handle.

I am not saying come in looking like the aforementioned catwalk model, but don't wash your hair the day before, or on the day of your appointment.

Wear a hat, a scarf or a scrunchie to hide it, but resist the urge to shampoo.

Actually, that reminds me of a young Scandinavian girl who had been living away from home for a month in London. Her parents came to visit her and were shocked with the state of her waist length hair. It was a complete tangle, a real bird's nest, right from the scalp to the knotty little bits on the ends. She said it was the London water, but there is no way that water alone could have done that.

They tried for a while to help her comb it out and had added conditioner and oil and goodness knows what else to get the tangle out before giving up and marching her down to the salon.

It took us over three hours to brush out the mess! We had to get the parents to buy painkillers for the poor girl.

They told us that they had booked a family afternoon tea at Harrods, and they weren't going to miss it for anything. So while they dined in luxury, poor little miss got the world's biggest headache!

So unwashed is okay, unkempt is not.

Take A Pencil & Shove It

Let's do a psychological experiment.

Grab a pencil and put it crossways in your mouth (make sure it's clean first – health and safety and all that), with the point of the pencil to left and the rubber end to the right. Now take it out and put it in your mouth so that the point is straight out in front of you, pursing your lips around the rubber end.

You were probably unaware that one of these actions forced your face into a frown and the other into a smile.

The original experiment that I took this from asked subjects to rate cartoons either with the pencil across the mouth, or with it pointing out. The subjects who had the pencil across their mouth, which forced them to *'smile'*, rated the cartoons funnier than the other group with the pencil forcing a frown.

The reason I thought that this was pretty cool is because it shows that small, simple and common gestures can influence our thoughts. If we are smiling, we feel amused and optimistic and our decisions change because of it.

I was talking to Kat about it and she decided to test it out on her six-year-old daughter, Heléna. Now Heléna is pretty good at reading, but absolutely hates writing and makes such a song and dance about having to scribble down even a sentence about a book that she has just read.

She even tries to edit the sentence as much as possible so that she only has to write the minimum number of words. Kat's a bit over this, so as soon as Heléna started whining about writing the other night, Kat got her to shove a pencil in her mouth and said the result was immediate. Not only was there smiling, there was fits of giggles and two long sentences were written.

Result.

I might just have to get the team to walk around the salon with pencils in their mouths.

Speak soon,
Terry xxx

P.S. You can take the pencil out of your mouth now.

A Tall Story

This morning, over breakfast, I learnt about the Mapuche people of Chile and Argentina in South America. They are an interesting indigenous race of people for many reasons. It's not so much that they fought the invasion of the Spanish and continued to be at war with them for 300 years, or that the women make beautiful colourful textiles, or that they are skilled silversmiths.

No, what really fascinated me is that they are the only race of people who do not lose their hair to baldness. Even the older generations retain a thick head of hair.

And what is even more fascinating is that this is not down to any type of genetics, or the environment: it is because of their diet. More specifically, it's because of a certain type of seed, which is only harvested once every seven years and is used to make porridge.

Sounds like a tall story, right? Surely there can't be any more discoveries to dig up?

Wrong.

Every day, scientists discover new species of plants, animals, fish and insects.

Every day.

Quite mind blowing, innit?!

I learnt all this while downing my first morning coffee courtesy of Mr. Daniel Field - the pioneer of organic and mineral hairdressing in the UK. He was in the salon to talk to the team about some new products we will be launching soon. But more about that later.

The big lesson today is that you are *never* too old, too experienced or too tired to learn. And by putting yourself in the presence of great people who want to share their knowledge, you get to learn big time.

Speak soon,
Terry xxx

Make Your Eyes Pop

I'm on holiday for a few weeks. I'm travelling Down Under to visit my family, with a stopover in Doha to see Kat and her brood. So what does a hairdresser do on holiday?

Cut hair of course!

Is that what is called a Busman's holiday? You drive buses all day for a living and then drive yourself around the countryside on holiday?

The beauty of my trade is that I can pretty much do it anywhere and anytime…cutting hair, that is.

I don't even have to have a lot of special equipment, just sharp scissors, a comb and a willing participant.

It's a great way to travel the world and earn my meals – and pretty swanky meals, too.

So that's what I did when I was in Doha last week. Kat lined up a few willing participants (herself and daughter included), who were in desperate need of a good cut.

One of them, Sandra, was trying to decide what to do with her hair. She was getting tired of dying it all the time, and her hair grows so quickly that the grey roots were forever showing. Trouble was, there was a contrast between her naturally dark hair and her greys, so when she stopped dying it her long hair looked messy and aged her. As for styling, other than tying it back into a ponytail, she was struggling to get it into a style that looked good. So, after a long and nervous conversation, she decided to go for the chop with me.

And this made her eyes POP!

This is an example of how going grey, with the right style, can make you look younger.

Oh yes!

Sandra has a great, fun and loud personality. She's from Toronto like my receptionist Gill, and it's bit scary how similar they are (it's too hard to cope with more than one Gill in the world!). But this new style really suited Sandra's personality, which is important, and she says the compliments have not stopped yet.

Party time for Sandra!

Speaking of partying, it sounds like the salon is having a ball without me. How about joining in?

Speak soon,
Terry xxx

P.S. Tomorrow I'll introduce you to some friends I met in the Middle East. Interesting characters, but I don't fancy their job.

Tin Sheds & Camels

Meet my friends Omar, Abdullah and Ahmed.

Actually, I am not sure of their real names as I don't speak Arabic and these guys didn't speak English – or the Kiwi version of English that I speak.

Kat was no help, either. She just kept saying *"La Shukran"*, which means no thank you, to everything they said, which by their body language was, *"Get on the camel, we will take you for a lovely ride, for a very long ride, and try to sell you to the highest bidder."*

Not sure if that was aimed and Kat or me. Either way, there was no way I was getting on that camel.

Then another guy popped up and his English was really good (better than Kat's Arabic). He told us he was from Sudan and that his camel, which was only 10-months-old, was a racing one from Oman. This guy had camels from Australia, Oman, Sudan and Pakistan – all bred specifically for racing. They sell for 3000 – 4000 Riyal each, which is a mere £500-£650. I guess the crunch comes when you have to feed, house and train it.

What got me though was that this camel was in a pen with many others in a cattle sales yard. There were between five and 10 camels in each pen, which comprised of a corrugated iron roof on posts. And then in the corner of the pen was a tin hut. This is where the camel *'looker afterers'* slept, ate and generally lived –

full time. They had no air conditioning, no fresh running water and no inside loo.

Now I am pleased that I'm hairdresser and a not a camel trader. And I am grateful that I was born where I was and have the opportunities that I do. But the conditions that the camel guys live in didn't stop their friendliness or their smiles, and they really did want me to get on the camel and have my picture taken.

Sadly, we didn't have much time, but I would have loved to chat longer to find out more about them. I am sure that as long as there is a need for entertainment, and camel racing is fun to watch, there will be these smiling guys in their tin sheds.

And there will also always be a friendly, welcoming smile at the salon, too. Come and see how big.

No camels though.

Speak soon,
Terry xxx

P.S. The camel did actually have a name, and they treated it like one of the family. After all, they were actually living with it. I would like to know how their clothes stay so white in those conditions. There's an advertising idea for Persil.

Sugar Rush

You may have established by now that I am a bit of a foodie. I love to cook and explore new foods. I got to try out Iranian food in Doha recently when Kat took me to an amazing restaurant in the new Souq (market). It was a feast for the eyes as well as the palate. The entrance to the dining room was a long vaulted corridor covered with tiny mosaic cut glass tiles, and the dining room itself was straight out of Aladdin. It was a taste sensation.

I'm not really keen on anything too spicy, and I like my food to know whom its mother was. I hate that kind of over processed reconstituted mush that has to be put into a mould in order to resemble what it should have looked like to begin with.

I was chatting to my friend Miriam a few weeks ago about her trip to Washington, D.C. We talked about food, as you do, and she said how she struggled to get a breakfast that wasn't full of sugar in her hotel. She said that it was a buffet style breakfast and was pretty typical at first glance. But when she looked more closely, there was a soft-drink (soda) dispenser for fizzy drinks in lieu of fruit juice, the cereal selection consisted of sugar-coated Frosties and multi-coloured Cheerios, and the cooked breakfast option was waffles with a high fructose corn syrup. When she asked for the 'healthy' option (there is always a token alternative on the menu, isn't there? Just in case of freaky health nuts.), she was given a granola parfait. This consisted of sugar-coated granola in the bottom of a glass topped with a layer of fresh blueberries (yay) and a large dollop of highly sweetened yogurt.

My heart slows down just thinking about it. Come on, people. A little bit of sugar is nice at times, but that is just excessive. Actually, if I were one of those fresh blueberries I would feel like I had been invited to a convention only to find that I was the freak entertainment. Whatever you put in your body is going to affect your state of mind, your appearance and yes, the health of your hair.

Anyway, I am now in sunny Perth, Australia and the food is fresh and tastes like food. It could probably give you its mother's first, middle and last name, too!

Speak soon,
Terry xxx

 *Tip: Embracing the grey*

So, let's talk about grey! As I mentioned earlier, one of my clients, Sandra, was debating what to do with her greying hair. She had thick, dark hair that was heavily grey, but she had been dying it with all-over colour for a while. She had gotten tired of having to get her roots done so often as her hair grows so quickly.

She wanted to know whether to colour the ends to be lighter so that they would blend in with the grey, or to have it cut off.

Now cutting off long hair is a big step. And going completely grey is also a big step, but we had talked about it and she took some time to decide. When Sandra made her decision to go for the chop she felt really happy about it, although she was quite nervous when she finally sat in the chair and we got underway.

But the result was just fantastic and Sandra is really happy with it. She loves it more than her long hair and wants to keep it short and funky forever. She has had no end of compliments and best of all for her, her husband loves it.

Now there's a way to keep a relationship fresh!

Going grey

Why and why?

Grey hair doesn't have to mean the end to natural beauty. There are many reasons to embrace it.

1. Your natural grey tone will match your skin tone perfectly, no more colour matching.

2. The texture and shine of grey hair can look fabulous as it is all natural, virgin hair.

3. To wear grey well you have to have attitude, darling. This makes you far more powerful (think Meryl Streep in *The Devil Wears Prada*).

4. It saves time. End of.

The age when you start to go grey is usually determined by genetics, so ask your parents and grandparents as this should give you a good indication. Things that speed up the greying process can include: smoking, poor nutrition, anaemia, insufficient B vitamins and thyroid conditions. Shock and stress can quicken the development of grey hair, but it is a myth that your hair can turn grey overnight.

Why does your hair turn grey?

Well, the pigment that determines your hair colour is deposited into the protein, or keratin producing cells, of your hair, which, like the rest of the cells in your body, have a limited life span. Once the cells die the pigment is not retained and the hair '*loses*' the colour.

In fact, grey hair is really no colour at all. It's the residual melanin that gives it its *'colour'*.

Maintenance.

So how do you keep your fab grey hair looking its best? Use the correct shampoo and conditioner for your scalp type, whether that is oily or dry, and yes, a weekly treatment will make that hair sparkle and shine. And if you require an extra shiny boost, a clear watercolour rinse in the salon will do the trick. Above all, work it baby!

The Best Blowjob In The World

Yesterday it was my receptionist Tendai's 30th birthday (ahh, the 30s – a distant, pleasant memory for me). The team took her out in Notting Hill to celebrate. They found a great little tapas restaurant on Portobello Road that fitted the bill for a walk-in booking of seven people…good wine, good food and great service. Trouble is, when it comes to most of my team, one sniff of a wine cork and they are off!

Last night they got so larey and loud that they started talking about the funniest things that they have been asked in the salon. Now they are not being mean, but sometimes they do wonder if they are in the right place and trained in the right profession.

A few years ago, a very beautifully dressed, poised woman came in. It was a busy day in the salon and she had a consultation with one of the team. They asked her how she felt about her hair and what she would like done with it. She replied that she was happy with her hair, really loved the colour and cut but could she just get a blowjob with lots of volume? Cue the salon falling apart.

The poor woman would have gotten a shock if he had carried out that request! She meant a blow dry of course, and he gave her the best one she had ever had. It has to be said that all of my stylists give great blow dries.

Speak soon,
Terry xxx

Welcome To Cork

My business partner Kat travels to Ireland every three months to hang out with a business mastermind group. Her travels to Ireland always seem to have a little drama to them, which she likes to tell me about.

Last time it was sitting next to a well-known celebrity as he picked earwax out of his ear with his finger and ate it…enough to scar you for life.

This time, the flight out of Heathrow was delayed for an hour as a heap of passengers from another disrupted flight were loaded on. Most of these passengers had been on a flight to Shannon – their destination – when their plane had to be taken out of service before it had even taken off. They were now going to be flown to Cork and then bussed to Shannon. Fun times. A few of them had been flying for over two days, after coming from the States, so you can imagine how tired and frustrated they were. By the time Kat's plane actually took off, everyone was getting a bit ratty.

The flight itself was pretty normal, but when the plane was coming in to land a woman decided that it was better to get out of her seat and walk down the aisle than it was to sit with her seat belt *'securely fastened'*.

One thing about physics is that it doesn't stop working even if you are ignorant about how it works. The fact is, if you are in a moving vehicle, your body is also moving along with the vehicle. If the vehicle stops suddenly and you are not strapped to it, you will just keep on moving. In this case, off your feet and through the cabin, probably doing yourself, and maybe others too, a great deal of damage.

Anyway, one of the cabin crew called repeatedly over the intercom for the woman to sit down. After the third time and no success, she ran down the aisle, grabbed the potential missile - the passenger - and held her down in her seat with one arm while kneeling down in the aisle and hanging on for dear life with the other as the plane hit the runway.

Was the passenger grateful that the fast action of the crew had probably saved her life?

Not a jot.

She screamed blue murder, demanding that the woman should take her hands off her. She said how dare she be made to sit down, and that she was going to sue, etc., etc. She made such a fuss that a male member of the cabin crew got out of his seat and ran down to help. Bear in mind that the plane was still rolling down the runway pretty fast with its brakes on. They buckled the woman in and made their way back down the aisle to their seats just as the plane turned at the end of the runway to taxi to the terminal. And as that happened the rather large male flight attendant fell straight into Kat's lap, squashing her.

Welcome to Cork.

The passenger had the pleasure of being met by the Garda at the airport and Kat had the pleasure of finally getting to the airport hotel and the bar (where she pretty much stayed for the duration by all accounts).

While it is an amusing story, there are people out there who are just stupid. The actions of that one woman could have caused the deaths of others.

Harsh but true.

She had no consideration for others and gave no thought to the consequences of her actions. And this is something we all should do.

This is also relates to your hair. After working with organic and mineral products for 15 years, I know that we do no harm and the consequence is shiny, healthy hair.

Guaranteed.

Speak soon,
Terry xxx

Frozen Out

If you have little girls in your house, or have friends with small girls, you may have encountered the phenomenon that is *Frozen*. *Frozen* is an animated movie from Disney that was released in November last year. It's been a sensational hit and is the first animated movie that Disney has won an Oscar for, gaining the accolade 'Best Animated Picture'. If you know the film you will know how it has affected little girls. They love the songs and aspire to be either Elsa or Anna, who are two of the main characters.

I am sure that many parents and teachers are sick to the back teeth of hearing numerous renditions of *'Let it Go'* or *'Do You Want to Build a Snowman?'* being sung around the house, classroom or playground. The kids are usually off-key but approach the songs with much enthusiasm

There has even been a Facebook campaign around how many *Let it Go* free days there have been in the classroom.

And what is Disney doing to cash in on this *Frozen* fever? Well, it's doing what Disney does best marketing wise - creating scarcity and exclusivity. They have limited the amount of merchandise going out to stores and are restocking only very occasionally. It has got to the point where there is now a black market for Frozen merchandise and it is the *'Mummy Currency'* of choice to score points with.

I know this because Kat has had our salon assistant traipsing around London to find her some stuff to send to Doha. She came back empty handed and I am sure that she had better things to do! But it just goes to show what people will do to get their hands on something so scarce, and with a high-perceived value.

Speak soon,
Terry xxx

 *Tip: Unacceptable in the 80s*

Back in the 1980s, when I had a salon in a small town in New Zealand, I was plagued by women who came into the salon and declared: *"I've just had my colours done and they say I need to be ash."* After digging into this a bit further they would add, *"I'm a cool tone and I need more ash in my hair."*

This. Drove. Me. Nuts.

You see back in rural New Zealand in the 80s, there was a plethora of bored housewives (the 'they' above) who were sucked into the world of network marketing and were flogging beauty products on a pyramid selling scheme. A few of them in my area decided to combine their selling with a bit of consulting on *'having your colours done'*, where they would hold swatches of coloured fabric against your skin and see what colours suited you best (usually based on your skin tone, but often just used as an additional tool to sell more products). Then they would tell their victim/client that they were either a cool or a warm person and advise them what colour hair they needed to have (failing to take into consideration what colour hair they already had).

Now I know that there are trained practitioners and stylists out there who are very accurate with choosing colours that suit you, and the methods they use are a bit more sophisticated, but remember that these were isolated women working from their kitchen table, without the benefit of even a YouTube lesson on the internet.

Then, armed with this information, and probably a little sample of swatches to take shopping with them, the client would go off to find the clothes that suited them and to change their hair colour to match. And the main term they had picked up was *'more ash'*.

The truth is, everyone's hair - black through to blonde - has red, orange or yellow (warm) tones in it. As hairdressers, we use green or blue ash toners to counteract these red/orange/yellow colours so that the hair doesn't look so brassy once a colour is applied.

The misconception of these Stepford wives was that they all needed to be beige.

Isn't it amazing what happens when a little information is given to well-meaning but misguided people?

And that is also the reason why it takes so long to train as an expert colourist. It can take years before we are properly let loose on deciding colours for clients. There are so many variables and colour dyes perform differently for each hair colour. It's a major responsibility for us to colour your hair, and if we get it wrong it's impossible to hide and emotionally heartbreaking. So I just wanted you to know that you won't find any colour swatches in my salon, and we are not about to agree to make you beige anytime soon.

Goodnight Kiwi

I grew up in the days when New Zealand television was only broadcast for a set number of hours. It actually closed down at night. It's hard to believe that now as we can access media 24/7, but back in the day, nothing was on the box between midnight and 6am. If you came home after a night out and wanted a bit of telly before bed, all you would get is that static *'snow'*.

Prior to the broadcast turning off, the *Goodnight Kiwi* cartoon came on and a little kiwi did his thing about turning everything off, putting the cat and the milk bottles out (remember those?!), before snuggling into bed and turning the lights off.

The cartoon ran for almost 20 years.

Yeah, I know, New Zealand: first to see the light, last to get multiple TV channels running later than midnight!

Goodnight Kiwi became a national treasure, and a New Zealand icon. For generations of younger viewers it was a much-loved symbol of staying up past bedtime. Kids in the playground would boast, *"I saw Goodnight Kiwi last night."* The fact that kiwis are nocturnal birds, not to mention endangered by cats, was irrelevant. I have happy memories of that cartoon, and I still have to suppress a yawn whenever I hear the music that accompanied it.

Sadly, the man who created the cartoon, Sam Harvey, died yesterday. He was 91-years-old.

News of his passing got me thinking about why we are here, because we are here for such a short time. What we do with that time is so important. Sam Harvey gave a legacy to the people of New Zealand that will live on long after his death. Others give a legacy to their community or even to the world. One of my heroes, Vidal Sassoon, left his legacy to the world in the form of his signature cuts.

So that's what I aim to do for you. My team and I will give you a service so good that it is my living legacy.

Speak soon,
Terry xxx

P.S. Breaking news from Doha. Kat has a visitor arriving from the UK today with a stash of *Frozen* goodies. Someone read my email relating to the film and took pity. In her visitor's words: *"I am now a sparkling moving monster of Disney kit."* I can see a very excited six-year-old this afternoon!

Spandex Sequins & A Flowing Cape

It sounds like a script from an old silent movie…

A woman is stuck on the tracks with a freight train bearing down on her. Will the hero get to her on time? Will the knots on the rope be easy to untie? Will the cameraman ever get to shoot more than the wriggling woman, the hero's face and the front of the train?

Well, for one Kiwi woman, who I read about in the newspaper, this nightmare scenario pretty much became her reality. The 22-year-old, who is deaf and has cerebral palsy, was on a level crossing when her wheelchair got stuck just as - as luck would have it - a freight train was on its way over that particular piece of track.

It was only the quick and very brave actions of passers-by Marzena Simpson and Mattieu Mereau that saved her. The pair couldn't free the wheelchair so tipped it over, with the three of them falling forward barely a second before the train arrived.

The woman in the wheelchair (she is not named in the article) was caught by the train and dragged along for a bit, and Marzena was hit around the legs, but both survived their injuries and made full recoveries. Both Marzena and Mattieu received awards for their bravery and courage.

It got me thinking whether I would do that. If I was in that situation would I jump in to help or would I be paralysed at the horror of the situation?

I like to think that I would do a quick spin and jump to the rescue in my spandex tights, sequined top and a cape flowing from my shoulders. Of course, I would do a quick glance around to see that everyone had clocked my physique before becoming the hero of the day.

Or was that just a dream?

Actually, that's similar to what it feels like when someone comes into the salon for the first time with a hair problem. Usually it is damage that has been sustained from too much processing, too much heat, or using the wrong products. I mentally don the outfit described above and get to work without hesitation.

Super Terry saves the day!

But it's not all a daydream. You can get the superhero treatment too. Just don't ask to see my spandex.

Speak soon,
Terry xxx

When In Spain

It's inevitable that in a salon with so many nationalities present, the talk often turns to food. Eating is one thing we all have in common, and it seems in my salon that it's not just eating, but eating *'well'*. There are many, many great restaurants, cafes and eateries in London, so when we talk about a specific type of food it's common that we will all have been somewhere different.

Of course, being who we are, we all compete about who has been to the best restaurant and then proceed to show off about why it was so good.

Following Tendai's birthday meal a few weeks ago, we started talking about the best tapas bars we had been to. Each one of us had *'the best'* example of one at X, Y and Z. As we spoke, each one of us got louder and more excited and animated about 'the one on X street' being the best in London.

Until Gleb piped up: *"Do you know where to get the best tapas?*

We all waited with baited breath. Gleb is a big eater and really enjoys his food, so this, we thought, was going to be a big reveal.

"In Spain!"

He didn't get the chance to continue.

Talk about stating the blinking obvious!

The poor guy didn't know what he had said to make us kill ourselves laughing. He just didn't get that this game we play is so we can show off our knowledge and perhaps convince a colleague to visit our recommended place, after which we could smugly state, *"I told you so."*

It's called *success by association.*

How it works is all very simple really.

We talk about something we like, and if that person likes or trusts us, and vice versa, we will probably try whatever it is.

Which is why I am grateful when you tell your friends about us. Good things are better when they are shared.

Speak soon,
Terry xxx

She's Giving Up Anyway

So, Australia and Australians.

Or, more specifically: *Australian customs procedures.*

In my opinion, this country has the toughest customs service in the world. So tough that they have a daily reality show dedicated to it on TV, which I believe is also shown on daytime TV here in the UK. It's one of those shows that you can't bear to watch because so many stupid people are getting caught doing stupid things that they know they shouldn't be doing. Either that, or they are just too stupid to even know they are doing the wrong thing. It's cringeworthy stuff.

Before we go any further, just to clarify, as a Kiwi I have to admit that there is a fair bit of competitive rivalry between Australians and New Zealanders. There are all the sporting jokes such as saying that you support New Zealand and anybody playing against the Australians. And you have to fend off comments like;

"So what part of Australia are you from?"

Reply: *"The New Zealand part."*

Or, *"New Zealand, the seventh state of Australia,"* which can be countered with;

"I'm from New Zealand, there's the North Island, South Island and the big West Island." (i.e. Australia) And then there are the sheep jokes and the jibes about how

we say deck and six. But it is a friendly rivalry and there are probably more Kiwis living on the Gold Coast of Australia than there are in Auckland.

But back to Australian customs procedures.

I was one of those 'stupids' recently on my trip from Doha to Perth. I got sucked into the craziness of Doha airport's duty-free. You have to see it to believe it. It's just like a market, but in an airport, and instead of tat it's selling high-end goods. But it's still crazy. So I bought a carton of cigarettes to give as a gift to my ex wife and the mother of my girls. Cheap I know, but it's the thought that counts. But my plans were foiled by the over zealous officer at Australian customs. Apparently, you can only take 50 cigarettes for personal use into Australia. If I wanted to take the carton in I would have to pay the duty tax, which cost 90 odd Aussie dollars. I responded no thanks because *"she's trying to give up anyway"*.

Yes, I know, ignorance is no excuse.

So, on the way home, after a trip to New Zealand to visit family, I decided to be a bit more prepared. A friend had asked me to bring her back some New Zealand manuka honey - one of the pure ones with a high UMF (Unique Manuka Factor). It's like gold dust this stuff and sells for just as much per ounce. I was in the supermarket examining my options and thinking what a good deed I was doing, when a little sign caught my eye.

"If you are travelling to Australia," it read. *"You will need to declare manuka honey to customs and it may be confiscated.*

You cannot take manuka honey to Perth at all…ever. Don't even consider it. If you do, Australian customs will do weird stuff to you and eat you for breakfast."

Or that's the way I read it.

It was a conspiracy and my friend missed out. But at least I wasn't pulled aside by those officious guys in blue and given a thorough search (of my bags).

Forewarned is forearmed and all that.

One good thing about Australia, though, is a magazine called *Peppermint*, which had the good taste to publish some of our work on its cover. Well, when I say *'our'* I mean that I sent our very talented senior stylist, Jean, to style the quirky model Lily Cole for a photoshoot.

I am obviously proud of Jean as it is his first magazine cover and he's done a great job. Now I just need to get my hands on a copy – are there any Australians that I haven't offended (or Kiwis) out there who can send me one?

Speak soon,
Terry xxx

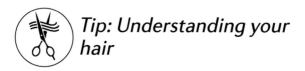 *Tip: Understanding your hair*

First up, the science bit. I love science. Anyone who thinks that hairdressers are just dropouts from school who are short on brain cells and long for conversations about holidays, let me put your right! We deal with chemistry, biology, physics and mathematics on a daily basis (not to mention counselling, therapy and a little bit of gossip on the side).

John Steinbeck, the renowned American author, wrote: *"It is my considered opinion that the hairdresser is the most influential person in any community. When the public goes to a hairdresser, something happens to them. They feel safe, they relax. The hairdresser knows what their skin is like under their makeup, they know their age; they don't have to keep up any kind of pretence.*

People tell a hairdresser things they wouldn't dare confess to a priest, and they are open about matters they try to conceal from a doctor.

When people place their secret live in the hairdresser's hands, the hairdresser gains an authority few other people ever attain. I have heard hairdressers quoted with complete conviction on art, literature, politics, economics, child care and morals. I tell you that a clever, thoughtful, ambitious hairdresser, wields a power beyond the comprehension of most people."

But I digress. I am going to give it to you in simple terms.

Here is hair:

The hair shaft is the only part of the hair follicle to exit the epidermis (the surface of the skin). The hair shaft itself is also composed of three layers.

1.The cuticle, the outer layer that interlocks with the internal root sheath, forms the surface of the hair and is what we see as the hair shaft emerges from the follicle.

2. The middle layer, the cortex, comprises of the bulk of the hair shaft and this is what gives hair its strength. It is composed of an organic protein called keratin.

3. The centre, or core, of the hair shaft is the medulla, and this is only present in the thickest terminal hair follicles.

Simple.

Everything we do (or don't do) to hair relates to these three parts of the hair shaft. Soon, I will also let you in on some secrets about the follicle itself, but at the moment my science lesson on the biology of hair is over.

You see, while hair is so simple to understand, what you do to it, or neglect to do to it, can create some massive issues: damage, breakage, ugly colour or frizz.

Your project is to learn to understand your hair so you'll know what optimal health means for you.

Four Weddings & A Santa

It is now some 20 years since the release of the film *Four Weddings and a Funeral.*

And, as you might expect given that it was such a hit (at the time it was the most successful British film ever made, taking £200m worldwide at the box office), it's now back in the news as reporters look at what has happened to the cast since the film came out.

I have to admit, that makes me feel a bit old (or is that because today is my birthday and no matter what I do, I can't slow down the years?).

Anyway, my tenuous link to that wonderful piece of British cinema is that one of our fabulous clients, Robyn, designed and made all the hats for the film. Even that gorgeous black one that Andie McDowell wore so well. Talk about talent!

Robyn is a great storyteller and told me one recently about her hat business. There's a bit of artistic license here as there always is when you retell someone else's story, but here goes…

Back in the days before the internet and the World Wide Web, Robyn had a collection of winter hats designed for a South Korean store. Think velvet and felt cloche hats, and the like. The store decided to show off the hats in a Christmas related theme. Bear in mind that this was a long time ago and there was no such thing as *Google*

Images to help with the research. The display was duly put together and the store people were really proud of the job they had done.

Robyn was back in the UK by this time, but one of her friends called to tell her what a success the display was. It had attracted every expat living in the city, and more.

"They've been queuing around the block for two days, Darling!" He told her. *"The display is quite a thing to behold. Christmas trees have been decorated with hats, fake snow, baubles, a nativity, reindeer…"*

So far so good.

But there was more.

Robyn's friend continued *"…and then there are eggs, rabbits and all things Easter, but the pièce de résistance is slap bang in the centre – a life-sized Santa Claus hanging from a cross!"*

Not sure if the hats sold well, but the store certainly made a name for itself. That's what happens when you don't do your research and just go with the knowledge you have, or have been told, or just go with a jumble of stories in your head!

It's a bit like not doing your research when it comes to all things hair. If you are not sure, or have never been told any different, then things can get horribly confused and go so very wrong. Which is why we take the guesswork out for you. Isn't it good to know that you're in good hands and won't end up like a South Korean Santa?

Speak soon,
Terry xxx

P.S. Speaking of *Four Weddings*, there is another link to the film and the salon: Hugh Grant. Stay tuned.

A Little Local Knowledge

Yesterday I was talking about the film *Four Weddings and a Funeral* (and a rather unfortunate Santa), so I thought it only fitting to talk about one of the stars of the show, Hugh Grant, today. He became an overnight sensation because of his role in it, and his career as the romantic lead in a series of formulaic films was launched. Not a bad thing. After *Four Weddings* came *Notting Hill* alongside Julia Roberts, and what that film has done for the area and, in turn, our salon, has been quite something.

Notting Hill is a funny place. Like many areas of London it has a diverse population. But the thing that is most obvious about it is that it attracts the tourists. Any given Saturday or Sunday, Notting Hill Gate tube station heaves with masses of bodies heading out to capture some of that Notting Hill magic. It's frustrating to be out then as you can't walk down the street without being stuck behind tourists, four abreast, stopping randomly to take a photo or turn around without looking. I have run over a toe too many times.

If I was the Queen for the day, the one thing I would change is the signage. It has got a lot better over the years, but it is still not very clear, or even existent. I find this particularly with street signs. They are often hidden on the sides of buildings, or on one side of the road and not the other. Or else they are tiny and in the middle of the street, which makes them pretty much useless at the best of times and impossible to see at the worst.

And the lack of signage is reflected in the number of tourists we get in the salon asking directions to:

"Portobello Road."

"The Blue door from the film."

"The bookshop from the film."

"The garden from the film."

Now, we are a friendly bunch in the salon, and in the beginning we used to give out the information freely.

"For Portobello Road, follow the road around to your left and keep going."

"The blue door is no longer there as they sold it for £x. The bookshop is now a shoe shop and it's on the right hand side as you walk down Portobello. There is a small poster from the film in the window."

"The garden could be any number of private gardens in Notting Hill, you won't be able to see it unless you are a resident."

But after the 20th, 30th and 50th time of doing this we came up with a cunning plan. Before we give out any information we say that we will tell them if they donate coins to our charity box. As an added incentive, we offer to give them directions to a few fantastic cafés or restaurants, too.

We get one of three responses to this:

A confused look before the tourist wanders off, usually in the wrong direction, without any further interaction.

A *"No, no, no,"* before the tourist walks out to ask the same question at the shop next door.

A big smile before the tourist digs around in their pockets for change. Then their map comes out ready to have pen marks drawn all over it as part of the deluxe version of the *Hair Organics Tour of Notting Hill.*

We like the number three tourists. They are prepared to give up something small in order to get something bigger in return. They probably realise that the information that we can provide as locals will be worth more than they can get in their guidebooks. And it's true.

More than you would know.

Local knowledge is invaluable.

Speak soon,
Terry xxx

P.S. Just like the knowledge we hold when it comes to making the right choice for your hair, whether that's about colour, product or style, it's worth investing a little something to get the deluxe deal. Otherwise you could be out there going in the wrong direction – just like our tourist friends.

He Hit Every Branch On The Way Down

Speaking of the film *Notting Hill* reminded me that I have another tenuous link to it.

Desmond Murray.

Now Desmond is a hairdresser, and a pretty good one at that. He has won numerous awards, appeared on the TV programme *The Salon* and is generally known as one of the top guys in the industry, particularly when it comes to black hair.

But Desmond is also one of those people who are incredibly talented in other areas as well. When he fell out of the creativity tree, he hit every branch on the way down.

Lucky sod.

He's a talented DJ and back in the day was offered hundreds of pounds to travel to Leeds every Saturday to spin some tunes for a club there.

He's also a skilled photographer and is sought after for fashion photoshoots and training courses.

Oh, and he's also frickin bonkers!

I had the pleasure (if that's the right word) to work with him for five years at his salon in Covent Garden, which he no longer has, alas. He was one of the most interesting people I have ever worked with. He had a huge amount of energy and was very generous in giving advice, support and training. I learnt so much from going with him on photoshoots and session styling at fashion shows. He was a great mentor and I think that everyone should have someone to learn from. There is no such thing as knowing it all. The thing about Desmond is that even though he was quite eccentric, he didn't suffer fools and if you came to work, you came to work and learn.

So what do you do with a man so creative and good with hair?

Get him to do Julia Roberts's hair extensions on set for the film *Notting Hill*.

Told you it was a tenuous link!

But the real message is that if you want a *good job done* you don't mess about, you *go straight* to the expert. And we're the experts in organic colour, so why go anywhere else?

Speak soon,
Terry xxx

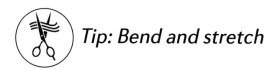 *Tip: Bend and stretch*

So how can you tell if your hair is damaged, and what can you do about it?

Well, there is a little test that you can do. But first of all, you will probably know by now the general condition of your hair. Is it soft or coarse? Dry to the touch? Frizzy? Does it not sit right or is it hard to style? Are the ends fuzzy? Do you have a lot of breaking hair around your hairline?

And you probably know that if you colour, highlight, shampoo, straighten or blow dry your hair a lot then it's probably damaged.

But here is a little trick I use in the salon. It's very simple, takes about a minute and will tell you all you need to know about your hair.

The stretch test

Wet a section of your hair from the roots right through to the ends. Select a few strands and take them between your fingers at each end and then stretch them as far as they will go. Now let the hair go slack while still holding on to each end.

What's happened to it?

If your hair stretches a further half of its original length and then returns to normal, then your hair is in optimal condition. Go, you good thang!

If the strands don't stretch at all your hair is lacking moisture. (This can also be the case for coarse or grey hair.)

If the strands stretch and don't return to their normal length, or snap off, then your hair lacks protein – the building block of your hair. This is often called chewing gum hair because it's like pulling a piece of chewed gum - ewwwww!

The good thing is that you can get optimal hair by doing certain things that will repair and prevent the damage.

"What are they?" I hear you scream?

Patience my little ones!

Entertaining & Strangely Hypnotic

My friend Den has been travelling through Singapore, and he has been sending updates of what he has been up to. One of the photos he sent through was from his *'office'* window, i.e., his hotel. It was a bit hard to see but there were hundreds of little dots of colour in the construction pit below him. It turned out they were workers and they were all lined up and bobbing up and down while waving their arms in unison.

Den said that this went on for a good 10 minutes.

It looked as if a very small section of an Olympic opening ceremony group had broken away and were *'dancing their own steps'*.

By all accounts it sounded both very entertaining and strangely hypnotic.

Den told me that it's called, *'body warm-up before work'*. Asian companies state that workers (especially the skilled ones) require a good stretching before starting work to prevent cramps and pain during the day.

You can find this going on in many countries around Asia. In China, workers do qigong as a group before their day begins. In Malaysia, a quick one to two minutes of stretching and jumping is practised. In India, employees do yoga before work.

Centuries of studies have shown that doing a stretch in the morning actually awakens your brain, helping you to work better for the rest of the day.

I might just have to incorporate this into the daily routine at the salon. Can you imagine the looks we would get from passers-by as the stylists, assistants and reception team all started bending, stretching and flapping their arms about outside the salon?

It would certainly attract a crowd.

Mmmmm, there's an idea.

Speak soon,
Terry xxx

Back Up The Rainbow Pony

It was my eldest daughter, Emma's 30th birthday last week. I just can't believe that my baby is 30! It's not so much her age that stuns me (and yes, the cliché is true, the time has flown), but how old that makes me! I can remember being 30, and it's as clear as yesterday (with a bit of blurred vision, of course, and those rose tinted specs). But that's not the point. I feel that age is just a number and I am not actually aware of my age until someone else points it out.

I like to keep fit and I swim regularly and competitively. I also cycle everywhere. It was actually at a practice session at the pool recently that a lovely Irish guy pointed out how old we were getting. He is a couple of years older than me and being from Belfast and Catholic, had a pretty interesting time growing up, and indeed, just surviving. Swimming was his escape; it was his time to have some normality free of the conflict going on outside, which involved constantly watching his back and avoiding trouble. It's amazing how swimming up and down lanes can bring a peace to your mind. It's bit like meditation that way.

Well anyway, we were sitting by the pool chatting about all things Speedo when he started telling me about how he had had to stop going to the swim sessions in the evening because the younger lads there were too aggressive when they swam. They were too competitive, too rough and had too much testosterone.

So that's why he was now swimming in the mornings, when the pool was empty, and he wouldn't get bashed about. *"Getting old, Terry,"* he said. *"A bit like you, too, I guess. It takes longer to recover from the aches and pains as you get older."*

Whoa sailor! Back the rainbow pony up! Old? Me? (As I started to rub my aching shoulder.)

As much as I mentally disagreed with him, the more I listened to his tales of growing old and not being able to do as much as he used to, the more I felt old.

"Stop this," I thought. *"Time to seek out some younger company. I may not be able to compete at the same speed and intensity anymore, but I know that I am fitter than some guys half my age."*

In fact, I just have to think back to the last race I took part in down the Thames. Close to the finish, I was stroke for stroke next to another guy, so I dug deep and found some extra reserve in my tank and beat him by but a length. When we got out of the river to run for the finish line he looked at me, and his face was a picture. He was a good 30 years younger and it was clear that he not happy about being beaten by someone older.

Anyway, my point is that age is just a number. Surround yourself with youth and youthfulness and keep your body and mind fit. Wise words from an old man.

Speak soon,
Terry xxx

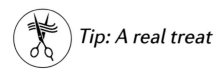 *Tip: A real treat*

Other than the stretch test, once you know what hair type you have, there are a couple of different things that you can do to improve the condition of your locks. These involve replacing moisture or protein. This is usually done, but is not limited to, external treatments.

Using the result from your stretch test you can now choose a treatment that is going to really help. This won't be the latest retailers' craze or something flashy and new to the market. It won't be a treatment that has pretty packaging or even a well-known brand that has been repackaged as a *'new and improved'* formula. It's one that is going to be of some use to you, and one that you will continue to use because you are actually seeing the results.

Happy little circle.

So, for hair lacking in moisture, you will need a moisturising or hydrating treatment, and an ingredient to look out for is wheat protein, which helps bind moisture to the hair shaft. For hair lacking in protein, you will need a treatment that contains different proteins that will bind to the hair. Words to look out for include revitalising and building.

You will also need to complement your treatment with the right shampoo and conditioner. I am sure that I don't need to tell you that a cheap shampoo is not only a false economy (as it is doesn't last as long as a concentrated formula), but it may also be stripping the very thing you want to be replacing.

Typoid? Is That Like The Plague?

There are a few things in this world that always happen to someone else, but never seem to affect you. You know they happen but they are so far removed from your own personal experience that you just shrug and say, *"Ah well, poor you."*

These include exotic diseases. You know, the ones that are prevalent in developing countries but don't affect us in the UK.

"Cholera? Sounds nasty, never had it myself, poor you."

"Camel sickness, never heard of it. Can I get that in London? Poor you."

"Typhoid? Is that contagious? Sounds painful. Poor you."

Wait a minute, typhoid? I've heard of that recently.

Kat called me the other day to say that her week had been like swimming through mud in a ballgown (a spangly one to be sure). Her husband, Kelvin, had been ill for over a week. Now as a Kiwi bloke, and I can relate to this in a Kiwi gay-blokey kind if way, Kelvin either just gets on with getting better with little fuss *("I'll be alright, mate")*, or ends up in A&E with his *"I'll be alright,"* attitude hanging on by its tonsils.

Well, this time it was the latter, and the verdict from the doctor was that it could be salmonella or it could be typhoid.

Whaaaat?

Typhoid, is that like the plague? I had to Google that one.

Yep, as I suspected, it's one of those diseases that is pretty rare in the UK, but is pretty full on in developing countries. Apparently though, there were 500 cases in London last year.

So, does Kelvin really have it? That's still unknown at this stage. Test results take some time in a hot, sleepy country. But if he does, one thing is for sure, his food handling career dream has gone down the toilet.

Literally.

Speak soon,
Terry xxx

P.S. That whole story reminds me of one of the only memories I have from my teenage years. Tell you tomorrow.

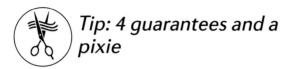

Tip: 4 guarantees and a pixie

OK, so maybe I am getting old, but by the tick of the spangly clock, so is everyone else. That's one guarantee I can give you today.

Another guarantee is that if you mention backing up rainbow ponies in your emails you will get responses.

Like this one:

Dear Terry

Thank you for this! Perfect timing! I turned 37 last Friday (I had a wonderful cut, colour and treatment from Gleb on Wednesday as a gift from me to me) and am doing the Jenson Button Triathlons (2 x super-sprint) a week on Saturday (for Cancer Research UK). These will only be my 2nd and 3rd triathlons and I'm super excited!

I'll admit that I'm definitely finding recovery a little trickier than I used to in my 20s, but I've found your emails detailing your achievements really encouraging, so thank you.

With the training I've been doing (and the wonderful hair that I now have) I'm hoping to beat a few youngsters and show them how it's really done, though I suspect that I will be beaten by several super fit seniors!

Perhaps you could provide a few tips from the wise on post-training/swimming hair treatments/maintenance in future newsletters/emails?

Katie x

The third guarantee is that if you ask me, you get.

Here is one tip for post swimming hair, if you have been in chlorine:

Vitamin C.

A little bit of this natural substance dissolved in water and sprayed on to the hair after your swim neutralizes the chlorine and gets rid of the smell. Don't use too much, though, as it can dry out your hair. And yes, we are working on a product at the moment that will do it for you without you having to think about it.

And the last guarantee for the day is that no matter how old you get, we have a hairstyle and colour that will suit you. Our oldest client is 97 and she rocks her pixie cut like no pixie ever did.

Even Tinkerbell.

Truth.

So get yourself, wee pixie, into the salon and you too can sparkle.

Bad Move From Start To Finish

When I was chatting to Kat the other day about poor Kelvin and his typhoid (he's okay, by the way, it was just bloke flu in the end), it brought back one of the only vivid memories that I have of my teenage years.

The boat trip from hell.

Let me tell you.

I was about 17 and went on a trip with the school rugby team to the Marlborough Sounds (think sunken valleys full of sea water, beautiful native bush, resorts and lodges far away from the crowds).

Don't ask me why I was in the rugby team. I hated rugby. Come to think of it, it was probably the tight shorts and the scrummaging. But I digress.

I don't even know why I went on the trip. It was a bad move from start to finish.

I do remember where I started to feel sick. At our lodge after we had been served a meal of greasy chips. This developed into the worst case of food poisoning that I have ever experienced.

Unfortunately for me, we were a long way from home, and as the Sounds are quite isolated there are no roads, just boat access. Add to that the company I was with, young Kiwi blokes on a jolly I had no chance.

The day after my food poisoning started, the group had organised a boat trip out in the Sounds, away from the lodge, to go fishing. They threw me in the bottom of the boat declaring, *"You'll be right with some fresh air."* And there I lay for the duration, amid the smell of fish and diesel fumes.

I just wanted to die.

When the nightmare was over and we eventually got home, I had a week off school. That was the first and last time I have been that ill.

And that's my teenage years summed up in a few sentences!

How sad!

Speak soon,
Terry xxx

Madam Got Evian

Once upon a time, a long time ago, there was a particular client in the salon, let's call her *'Madam'*, as that's what she was.

A *proper* one.

Now Madam had regular appointments with us early in the mornings, every Tuesday. This particular Tuesday I am talking about was like any other. Only one small thing was different. Workmen were digging up the road/footpath outside the salon.

Anyway, Madam is having colour on her hair and it is time to wash it off before it overdevelops and leaves her with a nasty shade of nuclear orange. We get her to the basin and at that exact moment the water to the salon is turned off.

Not a trickle.

Not a drip.

Not a vapour.

You guessed right, the workmen had cut us off. They had cut through a pipe, or hit the wrong button, or whatever excuse they have for leaving you high and dry without telling you.

So it's panic stations, and while I am out having words with the workmen, Kat is thinking, *"How are we going to deal with this?"* Madam starts kicking off at the basin, screeching about her hair. Kat reassures her that she will get water from the shop next door and everything will be fine.

I wish I could say that Madam demanded it be Evian (which would have made a better story), but she didn't. Evian was actually the only water the guy had left in the shop.

So Madam got Evian.

Now this was the time, early on in the salon's days, when Kat, *'The Queen of Everything'*, was *'helping out'* and learning about everything from the ground up. She was a bit put out by the fact that she was learning to shampoo hair (it is an art form after all, you certainly know when you get a bad one), and her motto is: *"Not born to serve."* But there she was, heating the bottle of water in the kettle to just the right temperature so that it could be poured over Madam's head.

Five bottles on and her locks were clean, shiny, soft and luscious.

What a huge difference *soft water* makes to the hair. You can tell when you travel if the water is hard or soft just by how your hair feels after you shampoo and condition. Sometimes it is so soft that it leaves hair limp, which is, I suppose, far preferable to feeling dry and crusty.

So, anyway, back to Madam in the chair.

All clean, she went on to get a lovely blow dry. Do you think she was grateful at the lengths we went to?

Not a jot.

In fact, she complained the *whole time* about how unprofessional it was not to have running water in the salon.

Complained about the fact that we had used Evian on her hair??!! Complained about everything! Actually, she was just *one big complaint.* You know those people who have nothing nice or positive to say about anything? One of those.

So we sacked her.

Yep, we told her, very nicely, that we were probably not the right salon for her as we clearly could not meet any of her expectations. She was a bit shocked at first. I don't think she had been sacked by anyone before. But she eventually got it and we haven't seen her since, which is a good thing, trust me. Life is too short to be dealing with that kind of misery all the time.

Speak soon,
Terry xxx

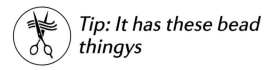

Tip: It has these bead thingys

It's the tiny things that make the difference.

For the last five years in the salon, we have been trying to get the water at the basins to run with high pressure, and at a consistent temperature. There is nothing worse than trying to rinse off a colour with a trickle of water after someone has flushed the toilet. And worse still, there's nothing quite like a blast of cold water when you are least expecting it in the middle of a cosy, relaxing shampoo and condition.

The thing is, we have consulted with a number of different 'experts' on this matter, and they have all told us that it can't be done. We even had a new boiler fitted in December (after the old one blew up), and thought at least that meant the water would behave itself, but no. We've had to employ a rule that no dishes are to be washed and no loo is to be flushed when someone is at the basin.

Not such a problem on a quiet day when there is only one person at the basin, but a nightmare on a busy day.

Well, you get my drift.

That was up until now, when a random Kiwi bloke (always the Kiwis with the answers, you'll notice) wandered into the salon to sell us a whizzy-do showerhead that would put an end to all our water problems.

Yeah, right.

Cold calling salesman.

"Heard it all before, mate."

But the difference with this guy (apart from being a Kiwi, evoking instant trust) was that he offered to show us how it worked. And boy, does it work!

Apart from saving us water, this new nozzle has increased the pressure so that excess colour just falls off the hair without scrubbing it, and both basins can be used at the same time. The temperature even stays the same throughout and there is no splash.

In addition to that, it also has these bead thingys that soften the water. Hair comes out nice and soft.

And it's no lie. ***Soft water makes for softer hair***. If you have noticed that your hair is dry, or you have moved towns/cities/countries recently and have noticed a change in your hair, it might be down to this simple thing.

What can you do about it?

A couple of things. *Firstly,* you can invest in one of these **water-softening shower nozzles**, or you can now get them built-in to your shower unit if you are going for a full bathroom refurb.

The second thing is to use a **clarifying shampoo** once a month. This bad boy works like an exfoliator for your hair and cleanses out impurities.

Simple.

Are You Ready For The Competitive Advantage?

Unless you have been living in a cave for the last couple of weeks, you will have noticed that there is an international sporting fixture on, one that features lads in Lycra spinning circular objects.

I'm talking about the *Le Tour de France* of course.

Well, what else is there?

As a cycling fanatic, I love to watch *Le Tour* and I was tempted to go down to the finish of the UK leg in London and see the riders. But I thought, *"Too many people, will just watch it from the comfort of my sofa."* Lazy I know, but I got such a good view of the whole thing.

These guys are absolute machines: increased heart size compared to other athletes, tough mental fitness and big pumping thighs (ooh er). They consume 8000 calories per day just to be able to race and keep weight and muscle on their bodies - the race itself is like running a marathon a day for three weeks.

A friend of mine, Anton, was the team director for the US Garmin-Sharp team during the UK leg. Pre-race, he was advocating Vogel's toast with New Zealand marmite and a team haka. I'm not sure if that plan worked (or if it would contribute enough calories), but it's good to have a little extra up your sleeve to give you a competitive advantage.

In fact, nowadays it's all about the competitive advantage, and because *Le Tour de France* has been so badly stained by the drugs scandals, it is good to see that they are getting more competitive the natural way – by scientifically working out ways to get more oxygen in the blood through cross-training, eating the right foods and getting the right amount of rest and muscle massage. This is a bit like us going back to a more natural way of hair colouring in order to achieve better colour, hair and health. Did I tell you that our highlights powder is made from seaweed? It's all about the competitive advantage, which is what you will also get when you know your hair looks good. It's the difference between getting that job promotion or not. Or, as one client told me, having great hair got her the *'man of my dreams'*.

Powerful stuff.

So, are you ready to get the competitive advantage?

Speak soon.
Terry xxx

Face Frozen In Rictus

I don't know if you have ever had one done, but I've seen plenty of those caricature pictures drawn by street artists. You know, the ones that you have done when you are a tourist in a big city somewhere on holiday.

You're in relaxed mode, the sun is shining, you are feeling pretty happy, there are new and interesting sights to see and explore, and there is new food to try. You go to the local point of interest, the must-see feature of the city, say the Eiffel Tower, the Brandenburg Gate, or the Golden Gate Bridge.

And there you see them.

They are always clustered at a discrete distance from the sight, but close enough that you have to pass by. They are usually sitting on a little upturned box or picnic chair with examples of their work, mainly copies of celebrities, which have been laminated and stuck to miniature easels.

And because you are in this relaxed frame of mind and you are on holiday, and your brain is engaged in the thought that you may never do this again so you've got nothing to lose, you turn to your partner and say, *"Let's get ourselves done. It will look great in the downstairs loo!"*

So you sit down and cough up the overpriced fee, and you put on your best smile as the artist gets to work.

Now, you know what you look like, you've seen yourself in the mirror every day, multiple times if you are some (for me, it's an occupational hazard). You know every wrinkle, every hair, every freckle.

You know how good you look.

You sit there with your face frozen in rictus and a crowd gathers around the back of the artist, watching them draw you. The crowd are smiling, or smirking, and chatting to each other. Some are even laughing, but you daren't move to have a look just in case you lose your pose. But now you are starting to feel a little less confident about how great this will actually turn out.

Finally, the artist puts down their pen/chalk/brush and turns the picture around to face you, and you get the full whammy of how you look through someone else's eyes, and as a cartoon.

This must be a bit like how the Queen must have felt when she saw her portrait painted by Lucien Freud.

And this was how I felt when I saw the draft of myself for the cover of this book.

I. Couldn't. Stop. Laughing.

Tip: Give yourself more time

I've been out of the salon a lot lately due to a case of sciatica, but I am feeling fine now. I have been touched by a lot of messages from people wishing me well. I have to say, I am a little embarrassed by it!

I'm not an easy patient you see. I very rarely get unwell, so it frustrates me when it does happen as it gets in the way of all the things I want to achieve in my day.

I learnt something recently about how to get more time to do things in my day, and it has worked so well that I want to share it with you.

Do you ever feel like you need more days in the week in order to get things done? Well, here is a great exercise to find out how you are using your time currently. It takes a bit of work, so it's not a quick fix. You have to be committed to it. If you are up for it, then read on.

First, take a piece of paper (you could also do this on a tablet if you prefer) and mark out time in half hour blocks down the side. Start at the time you wake up, e.g., 6.30am, and mark from there; 7.00am, 7.30am, 8.00am, etc., until you get to the time you go to bed. This is just for one day.

Starting on the day you are going to undertake this task (maybe you will start tomorrow?), write down everything you have done in that half hour.

So it might look something like this:

6.00am alarm: Woke, checked Facebook and personal emails.

6.30am: showered and dressed for work.

7.00am: Got kids up.

7.30am: Breakfast and school lunches made.

That's all you need to do. Just do this for tomorrow and I will give you the next step shortly. I promise that it will be worth it!

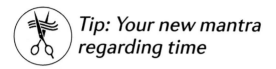

Tip: Your new mantra regarding time

So, did you get to do the exercise yesterday and record everything you did each half hour?

Did the results surprise you?

When I did this with a group of people it was amazing how much time we spent on Facebook, surfing the net and making cups of coffee, etc. And what was a really *'busy'* day ended up being not that productive at all.

Here's the trick to getting some time back for yourself. For everything you do, ask yourself: is there a way I can delegate or outsource it to someone else, or automate it so that it is automatically done for me?

My mantra: *'Outsource, delegate, automate.'*

This might not apply to everything that you do. For example, it might not be a great idea to outsource your children, although I guess school fits that category. But take the 80/20 rule that I shared with you earlier. Remember that 80% of your results come from 20% of your efforts. Make that 20% the priority in your day and the rest will fall into place. (Actually, I would love to know what sort of things you managed to outsource, delegate and automate.)

In the meantime, enjoy your extra day off!

Conclusion

Now you know a lot about me - more than you might want to! But I hope that the goal I set at the start of this book – to build a relationship with you based on trust - has been achieved.

I really do know what I am talking about when it comes to hair; it's been my life for over 30 years. You don't have to put up with bad or hard to manage hair. There is a colour that is right for you – maybe more than one. Yes, it is hard to find the perfect hairdresser, so here's the deal…you can now do one of two things:

1. Log on to **www.hairorganics.co.uk** and get my '*3 Simple Rules to Finding the Perfect Hairdresser for You*'.

2. On the last page there is a very simple form. Answer the two questions about the goals for your hair and your challenges.

   Then **make an appointment** by emailing **nottinghill@hairorganics.co.uk** or calling **+44 207 2296318.** We will help you to achieve that goal.

P.S. Before answer these, have a good think about this question:

If you woke up tomorrow morning and your hair was perfect, what would it look like?"

Biographies

Terry Wilson - Author and Co-owner of Hair Organics Notting Hill and Swimming (Drag) Queen

Terry has been a hairdresser for over 30 years but he's not counting. He lives with his partner, Jon, in London, UK, but still has an ex-wife, mother-of-his-children, Kay, who lives in New Zealand and his daughters Emma and Hannah who want nothing to do with hairdressing. While he is not making things happen in the salon he likes to swim, cycle, watch *'Masterchef'* on TV and cook. His most memorable moments have been trialling to be the hairdresser for the Queen, opening a salon in the Port of Picton, New Zealand then upgrading to opening one in Notting Hill, London (a real Kiwi *'pinch-me'* moment), and swimming a personal best sub 1 minute, freestyle at the Gay Games in Sydney.

Without Kat, Terry would have not even opened a bank account let alone have a successful salon, but would also have far less worry lines.

Kat Smith - Co-author and Co-owner of Hair Organics Notting Hill and *'Queen of Everything'.*

Kat is a mum, a wife, a businesswomen, proud Kiwi and half English. She lives with her husband, Kelvin, her six year old daughter, Heléna, and their fluffy white cat *'Pudding'* in Doha, Qatar.

When she is not running a business from abroad she likes to run, swim, and cycle (I see a triathlon entry) and is learning how to act. Her most memorable moments have been climbing a mountain in Borneo at 3am,

sleeping on an ice-bed in Sweden and serving a trespass notice on a convicted murderer in a small New Zealand town (his mum called her afterwards to complain!).

Without Terry, Kat would have horrible hair but far less grey ones.

How do you feel about your hair today?

What is your goal for your hair in the next six months?

What are the top three challenges that are preventing you from reaching that goal?

1.

2.

3.

Complete this form and bring it with you to your appointment at *Hair Organics Notting Hill*. Email us at nottinghill@hairorganics.co.uk or phone +44 207 229 6318.